Breath of Life

Breath of Life

*A Believer's Guide
to Healing, Wholeness and
Complementary Therapies*

John Huggett

Sovereign World

Sovereign World Ltd
PO Box 777
Tonbridge
Kent TN11 0ZS
England

Email: info@sovereign-world.com
Website: www.sovereign-world.com

Copyright © 2004 John Huggett
To celebrate the Silver Jubilee of Breath Ministries.

All rights reserved. No part of this publication may be reproduced, stored in a retrieval system, or transmitted in any form or by any means, electronic, mechanical, photocopying or otherwise, without the prior written consent of the publisher. Short extracts may be used for review purposes.

Unless otherwise stated, Scripture quotations are taken from The Holy Bible, New International Version. Copyright © 1973, 1978, 1984 by International Bible Society. Published by Hodder & Stoughton Ltd.

Other versions used are:
Authorised Version
Revised Standard Version
Amplified Bible
Good News Bible
Living Bible

ISBN 1 85240 387 X

The publishers aim to produce books which will help to extend and build up the Kingdom of God. We do not necessarily agree with every view expressed by the author, or with every interpretation of Scripture expressed. We expect each reader to make his/her judgement in the light of their own understanding of God's Word and in an attitude of Christian love and fellowship.

Names have been changed to preserve confidentiality.

Cover design by CCD, www.ccdgroup.co.uk
Typeset by CRB Associates, Reepham, Norfolk
Printed by Clays, St Ives plc

Dedicated to the loving memory of
Ros Griffiths
who asked many of the questions in this book,
and whose life shone for Jesus.

Acknowledgements

In writing this book, my warmest thanks are extended specially to the following people:

- My darling wife, Chris, who has faithfully shared in my life and ministry over many years.
- Commander Charles Hooper, Chairman of Breath Fellowship Trust, our 'Barnabas' (Acts 4:36).
- Mark and Lynda Lynam, who with us are expecting the greater things (John 14:12).
- Rev. Christine Haydon, Curate of Aylesford, who has given valuable support to our ministry.
- Brian Kendall, for his wise advice and for making a number of useful suggestions.
- Rev. Trevor Dearing, who first launched me into the public healing ministry.
- Pam Hambly, who at various points kept saying, 'You must write another book.'
- My editor and publishers, for all the effort put into producing and distributing this work.
- The contributors to the Foreword, for taking time to read the manuscript and give their impressions.
- All our supporters who have loyally prayed for us and encouraged us to blaze the trail.

Contents

Acknowledgements   6
Foreword by Christian Leaders   9
Prologue: Called to Blaze a Trail   14
Preface: Blaze a Trail for Jesus   15
Introduction: Prepared to Blaze a Trail   17

SECTION 1: *Why?*   19
Question 1 Instant Miracles   19
Question 2 The Unhealed   25
Question 3 Partial Healing   29

SECTION 2: *Who?*   34
Question 4 Unworthy Channels   34
Question 5 Overcoming Fears   39
Question 6 Spirit-filled   43

SECTION 3: *How?*   51
Question 7 Self-confidence   51
Question 8 Therapeutic Touch   56
Question 9 Meditating Rightly   62

SECTION 4: *Endorsement*   68
Question 10 Orthodox Medicine   68
Question 11 Scientific Proof   73
Question 12 Scriptural Backing   78

SECTION 5: *Lifestyle*   88
Question 13 Taking Control   88
Question 14 Natural Remedies   92
Question 15 Releasing Energy   97

SECTION 6: *Guidance*   103
Question 16 God's Clock   103
Question 17 Root Causes   110
Question 18 Supernatural Knowledge   116

SECTION 7: *Gifts* 123
Question 19 Being Sure 123
Question 20 Genuine Healing 128
Question 21 Different Gifts 132

SECTION 8: *Therapies* 139
Question 22 Questionable Origins 139
Question 23 Homoeopathic Remedies 145
Question 24 Acceptable Practitioners 150

SECTION 9: *Warnings* 155
Question 25 Spiritual Discernment 155
Question 26 Harmful Experiences 160
Question 27 Evil Spirits 168

SECTION 10: *Discernment* 174
Question 28 'Losing' Healing 174
Question 29 Spiritist Healing 178
Question 30 Deliverance Ministry 183

SECTION 11: *Tools* 191
Question 31 Prayer and Fasting 191
Question 32 Powerful Atmospheres 196
Question 33 Physical Sensations 200

SECTION 12: *Outlook* 206
Question 34 No Condemnation 206
Question 35 Christian Involvement 211
Question 36 Dynamic Vision 216

Epilogue: Healing the Jesus Way 226
Prayer: Healing Power 230
Appendix 1: Terminology of Healing 232
Appendix 2: Therapies and Practices 235
Appendix 3: Institutions Recognising Therapists 238
Appendix 4: Breath Ministries and PACT 241
Bibliography 243
Index 245

Foreword by Christian Leaders

Doctor Michael Harper

(Director of Burrswood Christian Centre for Healthcare and Ministry at Groombridge in East Sussex)

Browse the shelves of any Christian bookshop and you will find many texts about Christian healing. You will not find many which draw upon long experience within that ministry and distil out the practical essentials with such clarity. This is above all a practical guide, easy to read and comprehensive, yet supported by scriptural references throughout.

But it is also a guide to complementary medicine. John and his wife Christine, an osteopath, approach it in a positive light at a time when many Christians take a very different approach. Fundamentally the argument many follow is that any healing which cannot be explained by our current scientific model must, by exclusion, be spiritual, and if the name of Jesus is not invoked it must, by exclusion, stem from an occult or demonic source. But this perhaps simplistic view can be questioned as follows: can we really claim that our scientific understanding is complete? Why the disparity in understanding between the worlds of physics and biology? Biological sciences allow little for the science of space between molecules and atoms. The study of physics is not so constrained. This is important because it opens the possibility that healing changes may occur through mechanisms as yet not fully understood without invalidating what we already do know.

All of which raises the question: if we dare to let our guard down a little to accept that (for example) there may be a rational basis for the action of homoeopathy, which clearly has an effect but which cannot be explained in conventional terms, how can we discern what really is healing by occultic spiritual forces? Again you will find guidelines here.

John recognises the dangers, but what is most important is our willingness to embrace intellectual honesty in our thinking about complementary medicine. Christians used to be accused of something called 'God of the gaps' – if something could not be explained it must be God's supernatural intervention. But in this area it's more 'devil of the gaps'. If we can't explain it, it must be of the devil. John is well aware of the reality of the devil, and he has warnings for us, timely and important ones. But his fundamental premise is it's time to take a more positive approach to complementary medicine. I strongly support his positive approach. We will have cause to thank him when scientific understanding demonstrates rational mechanisms for a wider range of complementary treatments. It is time to be more open! Thank you, John, for your courage in leading the way.

Rev. Dr Andrew Daunton-Fear

(Until recently he was Rector of St Margaret's, Barming in Kent and Chairman of Rochester Diocesan Council of Health and Healing. He is currently Lecturer in Church History at St Andrew's Theological Seminary at Manila in the Philippines.)

It has been my privilege to have known John and Christine Huggett for the last fourteen of their thirty years involved in healing ministry. On several occasions they have ministered to me personally. Besides involvement in the Christian healing ministry of prayer and laying-on-of-hands, over ten years ago Christine qualified and has subsequently practised as an osteopath. This has led to the broadening of their interest to the whole field of complementary medicine.

This book draws then on a wealth of experience. Its structure takes the form of providing answers to a wide range of questions people ask about sickness, healing, complementary therapies and deliverance. The twelve main sections are each divided into three sub-sections. John's thoughtful answers, which are anchored in biblical teaching, betray much common sense and not a little humour, and include stories of many actual healings from his ministry, though with names changed to preserve confidentiality.

The Huggetts' healing ministry is unashamedly charismatic. It draws on the power of the Holy Spirit and uses the name of Jesus.

John speaks regularly of the exercise of the gifts of the Spirit – tongues, interpretation, discernment, etc. – not to mention healing itself (1 Corinthians 12:4–10). While acknowledging some mental illness is due to natural causes, he clearly also accepts the reality of demons, and is prepared to challenge any reader who does not to attend an exorcism and try to explain it otherwise! And he gives remarkable instances from his experience of deliverance ministry. No one should dismiss this because it lies outside his or her own experience but rather keep an open mind. John seeks to do just this himself over complementary therapies. Whilst he is not impressed with New Age teaching he clearly thinks that therapies such as reflexology are 'God-given and neutral aids to healing'. I am reminded of similar words used by the early church father Tertullian in declaring that Christians should not shun the medical science of his day just because it came out of a pagan society. John has much that is helpful to say too to those today who are perplexed that their healing is only partial, or worse, has been 'lost'.

No one with an interest in healing will read this book without learning a lot, and many, it is hoped, will be emboldened to get more involved with the work of healing themselves.

Alan Crook

(Author of A Christian's Guide to Homoeopathy *and a Methodist Elder and Lay Preacher at Crowborough in East Sussex, he was until recently a Director of Studies at the College of Homoeopathy in London.)*

I had not read twenty of the 300+ pages of manuscript before I found myself thinking, 'This is for me!'

This is an inspiring, motivating and empowering book, and I believe God will use it powerfully to convince many Christians who think healing is 'something that other people do' that it is actually something which must occupy a central place in their own Christian life and witness. I pray that it will be studied and given serious consideration by ordained and lay Christians everywhere. But most of all I hope and pray that it will be used by study groups in many churches, for John Huggett has given not just information but a well-designed, systematic study resource, with practical discussion topics following each unit, not to mention a number of very useful appendices. It is a mine of information, richly illustrated with examples of healings from John and Christine's fruitful ministry over the years, and well seasoned with good humour.

What a transformation we should see in the life and witness of the Christian Church if many church communities acted on the message of this book and became channels of God's healing power! This book demystifies healing of all kinds, clarifies important issues and offers answers to many honest questions. It has given me a vision that, I pray, I will be enabled to share with fellow Christians in as many situations as possible.

Catherine Francis

(A freelance journalist specialising in health magazines and Christian publications, she is the former chief sub-editor of Here's Health *magazine and was a columnist of the* Christian Herald *for several years.)*

For many Christians the rights and wrongs of complementary therapies have become a source of confusion and bewilderment. On the one hand, we may instinctively feel that the natural whole person approach of many therapies, which are becoming increasingly popular even with the medical procession, reflects a godly approach to health and healing. On the other hand, we hear alternative therapies being condemned as 'New Age' and even occult, and wholly unsuitable for followers of Christ.

As Christians we are wise to be cautious in our choices, particularly in areas where it's suggested we shouldn't venture. None of us can afford to be so arrogant that we don't take seriously the concerns of other experienced Christians. But at the same time we do ourselves a disservice if we throw out the baby with the bath water and rob ourselves of God-given means of healing. We owe it to the Church and to God to delve a little deeper and investigate whether these therapies really are incompatible with Christian living or have simply been lazily lumped together under the New Age umbrella without taking the time to separate the wheat from the chaff.

Rev. John Huggett and his wife Christine have spent many years working tirelessly, through Breath Ministries and PACT, to promote a balanced understanding of holistic therapies within the Church. So John knows well the questions Christians are asking – or should be asking – about therapies, and he tackles them with common sense and spiritual depth.

For those trying to make sense of the world of holistic therapies *Breath of Life is* a good place to start. Not only will it inspire readers to seek the healing God wants for them but also to forge a closer relationship with Him.

Prologue

Called to Blaze a Trail

Christine and I have seen people healed of almost everything you can think of. By March 1993 Breath Ministries were established as a registered charity and resource for Christian healing, teaching and training, and my wife was about to qualify as an osteopath. At this point we held one of our southern residential conferences at Graham Chieseman House, Chislehurst, then the Rochester Diocesan Retreat Centre. And there a significant prophetic word was given:

> 'The Lord is saying, "I urge you, My children, to blaze a trail for Me. For I would lead you into places where others would not dare to tread. I would lead you to be pioneers in uncharted territory which others have not really explored. There is no need to fear, because I will come with you and lead you there. It is necessary for you to blaze these trails for Me, to go to people who would otherwise not know My blessings, as they can know them. Therefore will you come with Me, My children? Will you go where others fear to tread? I will uphold you, I will equip you, I will give you all you need. But what I urge you to do is to blaze a trail for Me."'

It soon became clear that one main area in which we were to blaze a trail was complementary therapies. Following just one letter to the Christian press we were deluged with enquiries. Many were from Christians called by God to practise therapies but ostracised by fellow-believers who felt they were doing wrong. Hundreds of other enquiries came, and keep coming, from other Christians wanting to know about what's helpful and what's questionable in this area – some desperate to know the answers. The questions explored in this book are the ones I have been asked most over the years about both healing and therapies.

Preface

Blaze a Trail for Jesus

Blaze a trail, blaze a trail for Jesus!
  Blaze a trail, pioneers for Him.
Make a track where no one's trod
  But where He has gone before,
Moving in the power of God
  While He offers so much more.
Blaze a trail, blaze a trail for Jesus!
  Blaze a trail, for he is Lord.

Blaze a trail, blaze a trail for Jesus!
  Blaze a trail, sweep along your way.
Healing folk in every place,
  Treating body, mind and soul,
Telling of the Saviour's grace
  He's the One Who makes us whole.
Blaze a trail, blaze a trail for Jesus!
  Blaze a trail, for he is Lord.

Blaze a trail, blaze a trail for Jesus!
  Blaze a trail, bring His healing touch.
Not just learning of His love
  But discovering His way,
Not just talking of His gifts
  But enacting them today.
Blaze a trail, blaze a trail for Jesus!
  Blaze a trail, for he is Lord.

Blaze a trail, blaze a trail for Jesus!
  Blaze a trail, Satan move aside!
Lives transformed and saints renewed
  And revival on the way,

Signs and wonders we have viewed,
  We are nearing Judgment Day.
Blaze a trail, blaze a trail for Jesus!
  Blaze a trail, for he is Lord.

Blaze a trail, blaze a trail for Jesus!
  Blaze a trail, praise your mighty King.
Lord I'll take those leaps of faith
  In obedience to Your word,
Lord I'm here, send me, I'll go
  Till the multitudes have heard.
Blaze a trail, blaze a trail for Jesus!
Blaze a trail, blaze a trail for Jesus!
Blaze a trail, blaze a trail for Jesus!
Blaze a trail, blaze a trail for Jesus!
  Blaze a trail, for He is God!

Introduction

Prepared to Blaze a Trail

Everybody needs healing. Healing means mending, and today God is healing through His Church, through medicine and through therapy. Everything Jesus Christ ever did in His earthly ministry was with healing in view, culminating in His death which made possible the healing of our relationship with God. Yet in spite of its recent acceptance as a normal and regular part of the church's programme many Christians have not yet grasped how the healing ministry can revolutionise the church, if it is allowed to do so. And in an age when health matters feature in every newspaper many have not yet recognised their opportunity to contribute Christian healing to the wider community. Sometimes they see the possibilities but are slow to launch out because of the questions they cannot answer. In this book I attempt to answer the most popular ones, with the aim of encouraging God's people to continue the healing work of Jesus. This is time-consuming and costly but exciting and fulfilling, as we witness people made whole through the dynamic power of Christ.

Healing and teaching

Christine and I have been involved with healing for thirty years and, after I'd served as curate and vicar in six parishes in the north and south of England, we founded Breath Ministries in 1979. Since that time I have travelled extensively, lecturing at healing seminars and training conferences and imparting in-depth teaching on Christian involvement in complementary medicine and acting in a consultative capacity to leaders. Chris has often joined me in this, besides working as an osteopath and life coach. She has been involved in Rochester Diocesan Council for Health and Healing and was my co-author of *It Hurts to Heal*, the story of the birth of Breath.

Every good means

Through Breath we've brought healing with laying-on-of-hands and prayer. We encourage use of lifestyle, environment, diet, exercise and every good means to acquire and maintain health and fitness. We have ministered to people with a wide range of needs: physical, mental, emotional and spiritual, and witnessed remarkable results. We give the credit to the Great Healer. In 1995 we launched PACT – Positive Approach to Complementary Therapies – a branch of Breath, together with the first National Register of Christian Therapists.

A central ministry

I long that more churches should make healing a central ministry. Some do not know how to start, others get 'stuck in a rut', so need help to make progress. Perhaps this book can play a part in this. One of my aims in preaching, teaching and training is to encourage Christians to enter their full inheritance in Christ. We welcome the fresh interest in healing in the churches but are not content it should stay there. Of the numerous healing incidents in the New Testament only eleven took place indoors! Jesus healed most people in the streets and the lanes, and we encourage Christians to use opportunities in their daily lives to share His healing. So many people do not realise that God has so much *more* for them. This is part of living *'life to the full'* that Jesus spoke of in John 10:10.

New horizons

Our training days, seminars and conferences have enabled thousands of pastors, churches and individuals to go on in healing ministry and many other Christians to become involved with complementary therapies. Many have also found a new depth and exciting quality in their spiritual lives. This has been a result of my other teaching books as well: *Six Keys to Healing* and *Healing in the Balance*. My prayer for this latest book is that it will help to build up your awareness and thus open your eyes to new horizons.

Why?

Question 1: Instant Miracles
Why Are More People Not Instantly or Miraculously Healed?

In spite of the alarming events in the world today we are living in exciting times. During the ten years following 1991, taking the world as a whole, more people became Christians than during the whole of previous history. And in addition to this, again taking the whole world, more people are currently being healed through prayer than at any other period. Yet while throughout the world all the great biblical miracles have been paralleled in spiritual revivals, the West has only witnessed a small proportion of these.

Occasionally in our own ministry people have been instantaneously healed of conditions such as deafness, blindness and paralysis, but the majority of our healings tend to be gradual and unremarkable. So why are there not more obvious cases of the truly miraculous? Before looking at several reasons we must look at one put forward by some Christian people, which is not, I believe, the correct one.

Not today?

'God does not wish to work in miraculous ways', they declare. Some insist that signs and wonders ceased when the original apostles died out; others say that such things are only intended for times of spiritual revival. But does the fact that during some periods there have been fewer miracles mean that this was what God wanted? Or is it not because the church has failed during those times to recognise what might be achieved, and to act upon this in faith?

Jesus showed that God normally wants to make people whole,

and sometimes to do this in a miraculous way. The Bible is full of God's promises to heal, and His promise of signs and wonders to those who believe (Mark 16:17–20) has no deadline attached to it. Although Jesus said, *'Unless you see signs and wonders ... you will never believe'* (John 4:48), He promised that those who *did* believe would do even greater things than He did (John 14:12). And Paul writes, *'to another* [is given] *gifts of healing by that one Spirit, to another miraculous powers'* (1 Corinthians 12:9–10). If gifts of healing are in evidence today, should we not expect miracles too? Does God want peaceful healing services but not powerful marvels?

Intellectual reasons

A more likely reason for the comparative lack of genuine miracles in our own country today is that we have often been conditioned not to expect them. We ascribe them to heroic saints or to famous missionaries but do not view them as a normal part of church life. This is partly because we prefer to reason things out and explain them before accepting them. Like the scribes and Pharisees of old we are more comfortable with what we are used to. They must have been amazed when Jesus even interrupted funeral proceedings to perform miracles (e.g. Luke 7:11–17)! But such 'wonder-works' had a greater impact upon ordinary people than their own teaching.

Supernatural dimension

Today we probably spend much longer debating what miracles are and whether they occur than in being ready to perform them if the Lord leads us to. As a young curate I believed that Jesus used to perform miracles and that sometimes He still did this, but it never occurred to me that He might wish to work some through me. It was only when I had a conscious experience of the fullness of the Holy Spirit (Acts 1:5) that the supernatural dimension was added to my work. I still have nothing to boast about but I expect sometimes to see signs which confirm God's word (Mark 16:20) and works which cause people to wonder at what He has done (Mark 7:37).

Simple faith

Our cerebral attitude to such prospects as miracles is in stark contrast to that of the developing world and of more primitive societies where miracles occur much more frequently. In parts of Africa, Asia and South America widespread spiritual revivals have taken place, characterised among other things by signs and wonders. Often the knowledge and the spiritual growth in these areas have not been deep, but the *faith* present is genuine enough.

And it is frequently this simple but expectant faith that has led to miraculous happenings. During the Indonesian Revival of the 1960s many of the participating Christians were not well educated but like Stephen they were *'full of faith and of the Holy Spirit'* (Acts 6:5). Reading that Jesus used to perform signs and wonders (John 2:23), and that He is *'the same yesterday and today and for ever'* (Hebrews 13:8), they did not attempt to explain everything but concluded He would do the same things through some of them. The results were water turned into wine for communion purposes, the ability to walk on water to reach an otherwise inaccessible island with the gospel, and other miracles too. More importantly, these signs caused thousands to give their lives to Jesus Christ, and to the rapid growth of the Church in that part of the world.

Emotional reasons

Another reason why we do not see more miraculous happenings and instant healings in our own country today is discovered in the lifestyle that many of us pursue. With ever fewer exceptions we live a stressful and pressurised existence which – in spite of problems that people of the first century faced – is generally quite different from the environment in which Jesus ministered.

Inner restoration

Because of our fast-paced and frequently frenetic circumstances we require healing of stress and tension and healing of emotions. Many people have painful memories, deep hurts, ongoing traumas, and often some deeply ingrained negative attitudes, such as guilt, anger, resentment, hurt, jealousy, anxiety and fear, all of which are preventing them from enjoying full, healthy and balanced lives.

So the Christian ministry of inner healing, along with psychiatry and counselling, is much needed. But healing of the emotions is by nature normally gradual. My full recovery from depression in the 1970s took eighteen months and many varied things contributed to it: medical and psychiatric help, drugs and the process of time, prayer and ministry, the help and encouragement of my wife and friends, and, in the latter stages, the fact that I did much to help myself. It would have been too much of a shock to my system (and to my loved ones!) if I had been completely healed overnight.

Gradual recovery

Many other people who endure emotional and mental problems require caring people to spend time with them, perhaps in sessions over several weeks or months, before their complete healing is realised or before they can achieve a better quality of life. The change in their circumstances is sometimes surprising but seldom sudden. Persistence is required by those ministering. Jesus said, *'Keep on asking and it will be given you'* (Matthew 7:7, Amplified Version).

In fact healing is usually a process rather than a crisis. It is not a commodity to be obtained at some point in the future but a development of the work that God has begun within us. And one consequence is that we may not find ourselves expecting miracles.

Experiential reasons

If people's first experience of healing ministry is unfortunate – such as encountering an extreme or a commercialised approach to this area that is simplistic and dogmatic – they are likely to be cautious about the whole area of healing. If their experience is of apparently unanswered prayers for the sick they are not likely to expect miracles. If alternatively they have seen definite results they are likely to expect more. And if their own church is growing in faith they are much more likely to trust for the miraculous themselves.

Preparing for it

One church in Bristol was praying and preparing for a whole year before I took a healing mission there. They were all so expectant that they would have been greatly surprised if nothing happened! They were not disappointed. Among those healed were a man with a severe spinal problem and a girl who been unable to walk. Another man, who had had a slipped disc, ran right around the city! People's lives were changed and the church made a fresh start.

Preventing it

What can prevent the miraculous is, therefore, the opposite: the church or Christian characterised by unbelief, pride and fear. There are three main reasons why clergy and Christian leaders do not get more involved in healing ministry, and these are the same reasons why we do not see and do more signs and wonders for Jesus.

1. Activity

It's possible to be involved in so many so-called spiritual tasks that we do not make time to be still before the Lord (Psalm 37:7) or to allow the Holy Spirit to move in the ways in which He would like. Chris and I were taking a leaders' meeting at a doctor's house in Kidderminster when the Lord spoke through prophecy (1 Corinthians 12:10):

> 'I've prepared a table before you piled up high with gifts and blessings which are all absolutely free. But some of you here cannot enjoy these immediately because your hands are too full of other things. First empty your hands of the unnecessary and time-consuming commitments which encumber you, then you can partake freely of the gifts which I have provided for you.'

2. Apathy

Some people say, 'Miracles do not produce faith, the gospel does.' Others are sceptical of their reality or that we can expect them. But we must not reject them as part of New Testament 'mythology'. Miracles are only a part of the gospel but they are an important part. We are not to chase after them but we do need to expect them. Some people are unaware that the great things God has promised are possible today (Ephesians 3:20), others are satisfied to leave miracles to 'those interested in that sort of thing'. They have not caught the vision of how these can revolutionise the churches. God is not likely to use such people in working wonders. The ones He uses most are not those who are content with their spiritual growth but the ones who *'hunger and thirst for righteousness'* (Matthew 5:6), and who are consequently filled and satisfied.

3. Anxiety

Frequently evident with healing, it is even more so with miracles. Many leaders are fearful of what signs and wonders might lead to, or of the resulting criticism from influential or wealthy church members. Some are afraid of Christians taking things to extremes, or of being unable to keep things under control. But when a leader has the courage to take his church on step by step in healing ministry – even if he is not particularly gifted in that area himself – tremendous things can happen, even genuine miracles!

Miracle workers?

Jesus always worked miracles for the benefit of those in need, and perhaps because there were no blockages in His life most of His healings happened instantly. Although ours do not, God can still through us multiply possessions, re-create body parts and above all transform lives, thus causing people to turn to Him (Acts 8:6).

The gift of working miracles isn't magic: it is the ability to do things that cannot be done purely through natural means. Some things that now appear miraculous to us may be taken for granted by our descendants. The gift will especially be given to certain believers (1 Corinthians 12:11), but it's as we all expect more that we shall all see more happen. And our expectancy will grow as we keep close to Jesus, hear what He's doing, see it in action, and are prepared ourselves to act whenever the Lord calls us to.

Miracles seldom just happen. It was when Moses stretched out his rod that God parted the Red Sea (Exodus 14:21). It was when the ten lepers went at Jesus' word to show themselves to the priests that they were cleansed (Luke 17:14). And it's when we step out in faith as they did that we'll see more wonders done for His glory.

Practical discussion questions

1. What is the place of signs and wonders in relation to the gospel? (Mark 16:17–20; Acts 5:12–15; Galatians 3:5; Hebrews 2:3–4)

2. How would you minister to a Christian person who has been suffering from chronic mental depression for several years?

3. Which church activities might you cease to be involved with in order to give more time to spend waiting upon the Lord?

4. How high is the level of expectancy for healings and miracles to take place in your church? How can this be increased?

Question 2: The Unhealed
Why Are Some Not Healed After Much Medicine, Ministry and Therapy?

This is perhaps the commonest question I am asked. If there is a God and He really cared enough about us to send His Son to die for us, why do so many sick people remain unhealed? Again before exploring several reasons, we consider a reason put forward by many Christians which I believe to be incorrect.

Not always?

'God does not always wish to heal,' they insist. 'What about Paul's "thorn in the flesh"?' (2 Corinthians 12:7). But it's unlikely this was a physical condition (if so, it's an exception), since the word used to describe it as a 'messenger of Satan' always elsewhere refers to a person or an angel. The New Testament nowhere teaches that God's plan for the world includes disease: it certainly includes healing.

In Matthew 20:22 Jesus asks James and John if they are ready to drink the cup (of suffering) that He must drink. But in the same chapter, faced with a physical condition, He does not ask the two blind men to put up with their blindness: He causes them to see.

If we believe God may not wish to heal us we should be consistent and not go to the doctor! While sometimes we need to ask *how* He wants to do it, such as with old people, we can be confident that He normally desires nothing less than complete wholeness for us. And He may use any of the three types of agent referred to in the question to bring healing: doctors, therapists, or Christian people.

The right principles

Some people are still not healed because wrong principles have been applied to their situations. Let's look at two principles which are important in Christian ministry and often in medicine.

1. Every case is different
Each person is unique, so may have to be treated in a different way from others. Jesus healed one blind man in front of a crowd (Mark

10:46–52); another He deliberately led away from the crowd (Mark 8:22–26). The sick person will need to co-operate with God in whatever way He chooses to heal. If someone who is trying to lose weight asks for ministry, he must naturally expect to eat appropriate foods. If someone is tired from constantly overworking, she may have to cut down her commitments as well as receiving ministry.

I can miss out on healing by rejecting God's way of bringing it to me. Christians should not assume that, because on the last occasion they were sick they were cured without going to the doctor, next time they will not need to. God may wish to use that doctor.

2. One step at a time

One conference that I led at Llandrindod Wells came to be known as 'The Onion Conference'. This is because one of the truths emphasised in the teaching was that healing is often like peeling the layers of an onion, one step at a time. It's not helpful to dig through the onion of a person's life if he or she is not yet prepared to share at a deeper level (layer). Frequently it's the top layer that is mentioned first – the obvious things that most concern him at that time. But when he is ready he may share deeper and deeper layers, or God may bring things to light from a deeper level. The Lord's healing can then reach deeper into him and make him more whole. As in peeling an onion, healing ministry can bring tears to the eyes, for it can be a painful process. But we are more likely to see full restoration if we take things one step at a time. It's so often necessary, therefore, to discover each next step to take.

The right tools

Healing may be delayed or missed completely if those concerned do not find and use the appropriate tools that God has provided. There are six major keys to Christian healing. When someone has seen little or no progress, even after plenty of ministry, one or more of the keys may be lacking. Look for the appropriate keys, use them, and my experience is that something will always happen, for one of these keys frequently unlocks a door to the next stage.

1. Faith

It is not correct or wise to suggest that whenever someone is not healed it is because of the individual's lack of faith. However, when someone fails to exercise faith that can obstruct healing (Mark 6:5).

We encourage sick people to put their faith in the Lord, and such faith is essential for healing of their relationship with God. But for physical restoration the faith exercised by another may be sufficient. At Alton we ministered to a man whose knees were so stiff that he could not walk properly. Afterwards he was fine, but said, 'I didn't believe for one moment that I would be healed.' I assured him, 'Never mind. Other people here had faith for you.'

Sometimes people are not healed because Christians are not praying within their faith (James 5:15). We can be wasting time if we ask for things we do not believe for. So it's often best with someone who has terminal cancer to pray for her pains to vanish, or for chemotherapy to be successful, rather than her complete healing. However, when God has answered these prayers for smaller things our faith may grow so we ask for something bigger, till in the end we may see the person fully restored. Someone else may have a gift of faith to believe for a miracle (1 Corinthians 12:9).

2. Guidance
Some people remain unhealed not because of a lack of faith but because those ministering are not following the Lord's leading. They may need to know the Holy Spirit's 'map' for the situation.

Walking in the Spirit (Galatians 5:16, RSV) does not mean just doing so-called spiritual things. I can wash up in the Spirit but read my Bible in the flesh. I can do the ironing in the Spirit but pray in the flesh. Walking in the Spirit means being in the right place at the right time and obeying God's instructions. If I am in the wrong place at the wrong time, someone may miss out on a blessing.

So those who minister healing need to get to know the Shepherd's voice (John 10:4). He guides through Scripture, conscience, nature, other people, books, letters, films, tapes, angels, visions, spiritual gifts, supernatural revelations, doors opening and closing, everyday circumstances, and the inward witness of the Spirit (1 John 5:6).

3. Love
Doctors have shown that physical conditions may be the result of negative attitudes. For example, arthritis is sometimes linked with resentment. This does not mean that every one who suffers from arthritis is full of bitterness. But if resentment (a lack of love) is

present, that may be obstructing the flow of healing. If instead the sufferer forgives those who have hurt him or her and is freed from painful memories, physical restoration is more likely.

At one service there was a hostile atmosphere until some children were ministered to. People suddenly became filled with compassion (Matthew 14:14), and healings followed.

> *'... if I have a faith that can move mountains but have not love, I am nothing.'*
> (1 Corinthians 13:2)

4. Gifts of the Spirit

When someone fails to use spiritual gifts, that too can hold up healing. The spiritual gifts listed in 1 Corinthians 12:8–10 often unlock the door to restoration: prophecy, tongues, interpretation, messages of knowledge and wisdom, discerning of spirits, faith, miracles and gifts of healing. Some say, 'I could not do that because I do not possess the gift.' They are not gifts that Christians own but are provided when required to pass on to people in need, just as the postman doesn't own the gifts he carries but delivers them to others.

Many believers hold back from using these gifts, perhaps because of fear that they'll get something wrong, or that those who are sick will gain false hopes. But if correct teaching is given, and if those concerned are prepared to learn from their mistakes, it is better to step out in faith and leave the results department to God. It's easiest to do this in the small caring group. When Christine was first given a message of knowledge in such a group she hesitated because she was new to it, but, when she plucked up the courage to speak of a right foot, a woman's painful right foot was restored.

Once you step out in faith for healing, the love, words, gifts and all that you need will be there, for that's where Jesus will be.

5. A release of power

In Luke 5:17 we discover, *'the power of the Lord was present for him to heal the sick.'* Does this mean that the Holy Spirit's power was not present on other occasions? Surely that power was always indwelling Jesus, just as today it always indwells every committed Christian. However, sometimes people do not allow that power to go to work. In some fellowships there is plenty of faith and love but little sign of healing, and this may be because those present keep the power locked up inside them instead of releasing it into the situation through deliberately opening their mouths and hands.

6. A willingness to change

Naaman the leper was angry that he could not be healed in the way he preferred (2 Kings 5:11), but only when he humbled himself to bathe seven times in the River Jordan was he completely cleansed. Sometimes people are not healed through medicine simply because they are unwilling to take the remedy prescribed. And some are not completely healed through ministry until they are willing to admit things need changing in their lives. They may need loosing from spiritual bondages or to repent of particular sins which lie behind their illnesses. God does not ask us to be particularly holy before He will heal us, but He does ask us to be willing.

Practical discussion questions

1. Can you think of examples of the way in which the New Testament distinguishes between sickness and other types of suffering?

2. A friend of yours has been ill for some time, with no obvious improvement in his or her condition. What would you suggest?

3. Have you had opportunity to manifest gifts of the Spirit in your church or daily life? Have they aided someone's healing?

4. Is there any area of healing ministry which you feel is being emphasised too much or too little? How can this be redressed?

Question 3: Partial Healing

Why Do Some People Get Partially Healed but Never Completely?

There are some people who delight in stressing that Jesus did not heal everybody, and when He ascended He left many unhealed behind. Jesus did not chase after every sick person in the Holy Land, but no one who asked Him for healing was ever disappointed. Today a fair proportion of sick people find a measure of healing but are never completely cured in this life. Once again the first reason I shall examine is quite popular but in my view it is incorrect.

Not everything?

Basically it's the idea that God wants to heal us spiritually but not to meet all our physical and emotional needs. It is true that Jesus said, *'It is better for you to enter life crippled than to have two feet and be thrown into hell'* (Mark 9:45). But we've already seen how much He cared about the sick, and I believe He still desires to heal us in every area: not only our relationship with God but physically and emotionally, our relationships and circumstances.

There are many mysteries in healing, and when some people are not completely cured it may be partly because God is testing their faith, to turn them back to Him, to teach them to cope with their disabilities, or to help train them to care for others in need. But God's ideal purpose for each of His children is *wholeness*. This is not the same as perfection, which Christians will enjoy in glory (1 Corinthians 13:12), yet wholeness is the meeting of every genuine need as far as is possible in an imperfect world.

The reasons I've given in the two previous chapters for why we do not see more miracles and why some people are not yet healed, are all valid ones in answering our question. But there are more.

Because of circumstances

Many people in underdeveloped countries, suffering from the effects of war or famine, experience some healing but die without a cure. Even when agencies bring aid there are not always enough medical supplies available in time to give more than partial treatment to some people, and others are only able to receive palliative care. In short their circumstances do not present opportunity for cure.

To a lesser degree some people in our own country have a similar experience. In spite of the progress in modern medical science there remain cancers and serious diseases for which no definite cure has yet been discovered. In many cases a terminal illness is diagnosed too late to be cured. There is a fair proportion of sick people who have remissions of their illnesses but eventually die prematurely. Some people are ignorant of what is available, others cannot afford it, some are treated in a substandard manner, and some are classed as 'low priority'. Others have symptoms treated but not their underlying condition. Having a particular treatment may also depend on which part of the country a patient lives in.

Because of Satan

When things go absolutely haywire non-Christians are inclined to blame the God they say they do not believe in. Young Christians blame the devil. More experienced believers tend to recognise that difficult circumstances are part of living in an imperfect world. But while it's easy to blame Satan for things for which he is not directly responsible, he is definitely behind much of the evil in the world, and the Lord regarded sickness as part of that evil. While avoiding the extreme notion of 'seeing demons under every bed' we must not embrace the opposite idea that there is no devil. Jesus regarded him as a personal force of evil, and dealt with him face to face, using God's word as a sword (Matthew 4:1–11). Christians have authority to contend with him in the same manner.

Spirits of infirmity

One route in which Satan works is through spirits of infirmity, which have the unenviable task of making people sick. An example is the woman with the bent back, who, we read, *'had been crippled by a spirit for eighteen years'* (Luke 13:11). So another reason people do not find complete healing is because of satanic influences.

Chris was once invited to a women's meeting at a village church to speak about how Jesus heals. At the close Elsie, the elderly lady leading the meeting, asked Chris to pray for her. 'It's my legs,' she said wearily. 'I've had them in bandages for fifteen years. It's an incurable skin disease. They weep all the time.' My wife knelt on the floor and laid her hands on Elsie's legs to pray. But immediately Chris closed her eyes she discerned that the disease was caused by an evil spirit, so before praying for healing she rebuked the condition in Jesus' name (Luke 4:39). I believe it was because Chris prayed in this way that within a few days Elsie was healed completely. 'Look,' she said excitedly, 'my legs! I can actually see my legs! I'm wearing stockings for the first time in fifteen years!' It was so encouraging to see Elsie's joy. But suppose someone had ministered to her and not discerned the cause? Perhaps her suffering would have continued.

Because of selfishness

When Jesus encountered a man blind from birth His disciples asked, *'who sinned, this man or his parents, that he was born blind?'* (John 9:2). The scribes would teach that sickness was caused by sin, either on the part of the sick person or of his or her parents. But Jesus revealed that this was not the reason for this particular man's blindness, and He healed him without demanding repentance.

On the other hand, when the Lord healed the invalid at the Pool of Bethesda, He told him afterwards, *'Stop sinning or something worse may happen to you'* (John 5:14). In this case the physical problem appears to have been a result of him doing wrong.

There are numerous causes of sickness. It can be physical, stress-related, psychosomatic, genetic, hereditary, environmental, social or satanic. But in a fair proportion of cases it is brought about by sin, not only through sex or hard drugs, for example, but through attitudes such as resentment or jealousy.

Repentance

Once it becomes clear in Christian ministry that someone is not finding complete physical healing on account of selfishness, the person should be gently encouraged to repent of particular sins and to crucify them (Romans 6:11). Paul wrote, *'we take captive every thought to make it obedient to Christ'* (2 Corinthians 10:5).

A man was once healed of pain in his back, stomach and joints, but he wondered why he still could not move his neck. Not long after this he went to a church service and heard a sermon about how we need to surrender every area of our lives to Christ (Romans 12:1). As he listened he yielded it all to the Lord, and in that very moment he felt his neck freed from pain. The healing was completed.

Obedience

On some occasions people are only partially healed because they do not take the opportunities that God places before them. A lady attended one of our healing services and later she wrote to us:

'At Hildenborough I had a slight throat problem. Stupidly I didn't come out for ministry and it got worse. I had trouble in my chest and head. Even with cough medicine and with much seeking of the Lord, I was not overcoming. Then eventually I realised I had been told about a very sick person and, having promised to put him in touch with you, had selfishly not yet done so. As soon as I obeyed I knew again the flow of living waters that Jesus talks about (John 7:37–39). Hallelujah!'

It's not only selfishness on the part of the person in need that can hold up complete healing. Sometimes it happens because those ministering do not persist in following things through. If you are unable to do this yourself, perhaps you can recommend someone else more experienced in the fields of ministry, medicine or therapy.

As we persevere in prayer (Luke 11:5–8) we'll often find our faith increasing (Luke 17:5). As we advance, believing that we're equipped, we'll find that we are. The more we use the gifts of the Spirit, the more they will increase in us. The more we apply the keys to healing, the more doors will Jesus open through us. And one of the results should be that more people experience their total healing.

Practical discussion questions

1. What are some of the obstacles to healing in people's lives and in the church to which you belong? (E.g. Mark 9:23–24, 28–29)

2. In what circumstances might it be better to pray for a sick person's relationship with the Lord than his or her physical healing?

3. On what occasions might you find it necessary to bind Satan or one of his agents from a person or place? (Matthew 18:18)

4. Do you know any 'half-healed' people? How might you help to take them further towards complete wholeness? (Mark 8:22–26)

SECTION 2

Who?

Question 4: Unworthy Channels
Should the Flaws in My Life Prevent Me from Bringing Healing?

Not usually, because if you're a Christian Jesus is calling you personally to bring healing along with preaching the gospel (Luke 10:9). There are four types of people that the New Testament speaks of as bringing healing: physicians (Mark 2:17), Christian leaders (James 5:14), those exercising gifts or ministries of healing (1 Corinthians 12:9 and 28), and ordinary believers who may not fall into any of these categories (Mark 16:17–18). If you are a Christian you are commissioned to share healing in some way.

The clogged drainpipe

Since Jesus is the great Healer, Christine and I prefer to think of ourselves as the ministers, agents or channels of His healing. One lady to whom we ministered spoke of us as 'God's drainpipes'. And this comparison is similar to the one envisaged by Paul in 2 Corinthians 4:7, where he explains,

> *'But we have this treasure in jars of clay to show that this all-surpassing power is from God and not from us.'*

The 'earthen vessels' through which the Lord has chosen to convey healing are always imperfect. We shall never be worthy enough and yet our God still wants to use each one of us! For on earth, as the well-known saying states, 'He has no hands but our hands to do his work today'.

If you think you have failed Him too much to be used in this way, remember the sort of people He chose to be leaders in His work: Jacob was a deceiver (Genesis 27:19); Moses was a murderer

(Exodus 2:12); David was an adulterer (2 Samuel 11); and Jonah was a coward (Jonah 1:3). James and John had vile tempers (Mark 3:17) and Peter disowned the Lord three times running (Luke 22:54ff.). Paul saw himself as less than the least of God's people (Ephesians 3:8). Be encouraged! Remember that a certain amount of water can still get through a clogged drainpipe. And however much you have failed the Lord, that's no reason for you not to be used to bring healing.

The cleansing blood

If, however, you are aware of particular things in your life at this moment that are grieving the Lord, it is necessary for you to confess and be cleansed of these before ministering, so that you are as clean a channel as possible when bringing His touch.

I love the 'windscreen wiper verse', 1 John 1:7:

> *'But if we walk in the light, as he is in the light* [if we honestly, openly and fully expose our inner selves with no attempt at pretence or hypocrisy], *we have fellowship with one another, and the blood of Jesus, his Son, purifies us from all sin* [literally "goes on cleansing us", like the wipers which keep sweeping across a vehicle's windscreen].'

It's also necessary, however, for those who would minister healing to be as much as is possible in right relationships with other people too. This is not always easy, even with fellow believers:

> 'To live above with the saints I love,
>   Oh, that will be glory!
> To live below with the saints I know,
>   Well, that's another story!'

But provided we are willing for reconciliation, and do not hold grudges in our hearts, we can still be used as God's drainpipes – even if right now those we've hurt will not accept our apologies.

The close relative

In church meetings healing ministry is under the authority of the leaders and they appoint teams and individuals to do it. We also encourage Christians and church leaders to receive training in this ministry so that they are better prepared and equipped to deal with the many different situations and questions that arise.

But you do not have to be trained before ministering informally, however conscious you are of faults. If a relative enters your home and complains of pain, you can use the opportunity to share about how God has healed others and to offer ministry. Even non-Christians are often grateful for this, and even if they refuse the offer they will become aware that you care. If you say, 'Jesus used to touch people. Would you mind if I place my hands on you while I pray?' this can add to the effectiveness of the ministry.

Giving more ministry

We often encourage Christians who attend our healing services to continue the ministry to their relatives afterwards. Here is a letter received from a man two months after a meeting at Ipswich:

> 'God has healed my leg which I broke and have had much pain in for forty-eight years. The doctors told me I'd have to live with it. I've had painkillers, therapy, and a micro tens machine. But after going out for prayer at your service I fell to the ground and did feel relief of pain. But Sunday morning the pain was back and my son prayed for me. It was worse this time, and all that week it was bad. The next Saturday my wife had to pray for me in bed as I couldn't bear the pain. I remembered you saying, "Keep on asking", which is what we did. Praise the Lord, by the Monday the pain had gone, and I am now completely free from it.'

Getting someone else

There are, however, exceptions to every rule, and we have found that the close relative is not the best person to help when the healing required is that of someone's relationship with God. This is because the non-Christian often knows the Christian relative too well, including his or her faults! We know of many Christian wives who have been longing for their husbands to trust the Lord, and sometimes praying for this to happen when they don't believe it will! What is frequently more effective is for an unrelated Christian man to befriend the husband. In time this may lead to his conversion.

Don't hold back till all your needs are met

Sometimes a person may be too ill or weak to attempt any healing ministry, but generally speaking we do not need to wait until our own problems are solved before ministering to the needs of others.

Many churches have discovered the value of sharing their problems with one another in the fellowship, as well as their blessings. This presents an obvious opportunity for the laying-on-of-hands. A good place to start ministering is in the small caring group, which hopefully will forgive you when you make mistakes. It is probably easier for the beginner to lay on hands in this context rather than in the large service. Leaders need to look out for those who would dominate the group, and anyone who cannot keep confidences, but also for those who would make the best future leaders, and to encourage those who manifest particular gifts.

Don't hold back for fear of making mistakes – they are necessary! I have learned more about healing from four particular sources: the Lord Himself as He healed in the Gospels, the Bible, other Christian teachers and their writings, and my own mistakes!

Don't hold out once the Holy Spirit prompts you

Because of their feelings of inadequacy or inexperience certain Christians hold back from ministering the laying-on-of-hands as they are unsure of what to say. But the wonderful promise that Jesus gave to His disciples for when they would be persecuted can be applied to any situation where we are lost for words:

> '... do not worry about what to say or how to say it. At that time you will be given what to say, for it will not be you speaking, but the Spirit of your Father speaking through you.'
>
> (Matthew 10:19–20)

Satan is 'the accuser of the brethren' (see Revelation 12:10), and he will do everything he can to make Christians feel guilty and unworthy, and so prevent them from launching out in healing ministry. He particularly seems to hate the power in the laying-on-of-hands. One of his strategies is to get us 'almost there but not quite' (cf. Acts 26:28). He is perfectly happy if we learn about

God's love as long as we do not discover His will, perfectly content if we talk about the gifts of the Holy Spirit as long as we do not use them to bring healing.

Going into the water

Jesus once told Simon Peter to *'launch out into the deep'* in his boat (Luke 5:4, AV). Sometimes we are 'pushed in at the deep end', as I was one evening in 1975 at St Paul's Church, Hainault, in Essex. Rev. Trevor Dearing suddenly announced that he believed the Lord was calling me into a healing ministry. I was almost immediately faced with queues and queues of people in need, waiting patiently for the laying-on-of-hands. I am so glad that Jesus was working through me, or I'd have given up doing this ministry years ago!

But, before Jesus told Peter to launch out, '[He] *asked him to put out a little from shore'* (Luke 5:3). At other times God calls people to move gradually into ministry before getting deeply involved. He leads and teaches them step by step, like Ezekiel, who first found himself moving in water ankle-deep, then knee-deep, next up to the waist, and finally deep enough to swim in (Ezekiel 47:3–5). Step into the water, and trust the Lord to work through you too.

What holds Christians back most from launching out in these ways is the fear of man, and what drives them on is the fullness of the Holy Spirit. These are the subjects of the next two chapters.

Practical discussion questions

1. How can a Christian leader, with no personal experience of gifts of healing, take his church forward in this ministry?

2. Have you any experience of healing ministry taking place in your home? What encouragements and problems can this bring?

3. Do you belong to a small Christian group? What opportunities are there in it for praying for the sick or people in need?

4. What mistakes have you and your church made in the realm of healing? How would you try to do things differently next time?

Question 5: Overcoming Fears

How Can We Overcome Our Fears of Other People?

This is an honest question to ask, because the person asking it recognises that fear of man is a frequent reason for not getting involved in the healing ministry. Particular fears that Christians have include especially fear of what other people think, appearing self-righteous or super-spiritual, diagnosing the problem wrongly, not knowing what to say, how to pray or how to proceed, offering false hopes or giving the wrong impression, finding it impossible to answer relevant questions, getting out of their depth, being ridiculed, and a genuine fear of events escalating out of control.

Facing up to them

The first step is to face up to our fears and not cover them up. God once prompted me to offer four sessions to a college lecturer who had asked for ministry. Dave was a Christian suffering from painful memories and fears. At the first session I prayed about his childhood, at the second his teenage years, and at the third I intended to pray about his married life. But just before it I had an impression of a pack of playing cards, with the jack, or knave, uppermost. I asked Dave if this meant anything to him and he replied, 'Yes. The name of the house where I lived as a young child was Knave's Knoll.' I gathered from this that instead of praying about his marriage I should go back and pray again about his early childhood. As I did, whenever I mentioned a particular incident he flung up his hands in front of his face, terrified, as though as to ward off something that he could see. So I then encouraged him to face up to it, and in his imagination to take the Lord with him through it. He did, and found a new freedom.

'Why are you so afraid?' (Matthew 8:26)

The commonest command in the Bible is 'Don't be afraid'. It comes 366 times. Paul wrote,

> *'For God did not give us a spirit of timidity, but a spirit of power, of love and of self-discipline.'*   (2 Timothy 1:7)

But some Christians hide their fears. Rachel, who attended some of our training days, once woke in the night and the Lord impressed upon her a picture of a key. He showed her that her friend Lorraine was the key to her other friend Rebecca's problems. When Rachel shared this with Rebecca she said she already knew this, but had been too frightened to share it. Only when the Lord had brought these things to light was she able to overcome her fears.

Fixing our eyes upon Jesus

Here's the second secret in overcoming our fears:

> *'Let us fix our eyes on Jesus, the author and perfecter of our faith.'*
> (Hebrews 12:2)

In a powerful healing meeting the enemy will do everything he can to take our eyes off the Lord, so I have often encouraged people present to hold in their minds a picture of Jesus. Once, after I'd suggested picturing Him on His throne, a lady told me how she had found it so helpful while driving. The constant reminder that He's still in control helped her view her fears in proper perspective.

A hymn sheet once included the title 'Our God resigns'. Fortunately, it was a printer's error, of course: our God undoubtedly reigns!

'Why do you worry?' (Matthew 6:28)

A quick glance at the list of fears I mentioned reminds us that they are all the result of looking too hard at ourselves. If, for example, we fear what other people might think, we are worrying about our own reputations rather than obeying the Lord who *'made himself of no reputation'* (Philippians 2:7, AV).

Christine and I once realised that we had to get past the point of worrying about what others think. This does not mean that we had no respect for their opinions, but we decided that, if we were sure the Lord was calling us to do something, we would go ahead with this whatever people said or appeared to think. In making major decisions we would seek confirmation from others, but our desire was that *'in everything **He** might have the supremacy'* (Colossians 1:18).

Turn your eyes upon Jesus

Turn your eyes upon Jesus when you are unaware of what to say to someone. For ten years Sandra had tried to interest her neighbour Louise in going to church, but without success. She was fearful of mentioning the subject to her any more. One day Sandra read James 1:5 in The Living Bible:

> *'If you want to know what God wants you to do ask him, and he will gladly tell you, for he is always ready to give a generous supply of wisdom to all who ask him. He will not resent it.'*

Acting on this, Sandra asked the Lord what she should say to her neighbour. Instantly there came into her mind just three words: 'Don't be afraid.' When Sandra next had opportunity to talk to Louise she hesitantly shared those words. 'How did you know?' asked Louise. 'You're right. Today a letter arrived telling me that I'm to have a serious operation, and I am terribly afraid.' That was the beginning of Louise's conversion.

Turn your eyes upon Jesus when you have made a mistake in healing ministry and feel apprehensive that you could do the same again. When Chris and I first took up horse-riding we soon noticed that riders who came off their horses and were badly shaken up usually mounted them again almost straightaway, thus minimising the fears and anxieties that might have arisen as a result of the shock.

Finding help from our brothers

The next secret of overcoming our fears is to share them and pray about them with those Christian friends who we reckon are on the same spiritual wavelength and most understand us. Alternatively we may wish to share with someone outside our own fellowship but who has experience in healing:

> *'Carry each other's burdens, and in this way you will fulfil the law of Christ.'* (Galatians 6:2)

Receiving ministry

In particular we can receive ministry ourselves for our fears. We can mention the obvious ones, and the Holy Spirit will frequently bring to light subconscious ones that are not immediately clear. A man at Aldershot constantly stuttered. Frequently he could not get words out at all. His real problem was subconscious fear. We ministered to him for this and his mind and tongue were set free.

Revealing fears

Subconscious fear may be a mental attitude that needs healing. It was a chief characteristic of my depression. Alternatively it may be an evil spirit of fear that needs to be removed or cast out.

Many of our deepest fears are often rooted in frightening experiences, unhealthy teaching or stressful relationships. When we lived at Huddersfield a Christian lady named Maureen, who was forty and unmarried, came to our home. Although much used in the gift of prophecy, she had a fear of approaching men. 'It's because I was molested by a man when I was aged eleven,' she confided. Chris and I encouraged her to relive the agonising scene, set her free in Jesus' name from the man who had molested her, and asked God to heal the painful memories and all the harmful effects of the incident. Over a short period Maureen was delivered from this particular fear and she became free to relate to men in a new way.

Reassurance offered

Before some people can be delivered from their fears they will need reassurance of how much God loves them personally, perhaps because they are very conscious of how unworthy they are. This in turn may be because they have at some stage been 'put down' by a dominating parent, or made to feel small by a Christian leader. Jesus once said to His disciples,

> *'So don't be afraid; you are worth more than many sparrows.'*
> (Matthew 10:31)

Be assured that if you receive afresh God's perfect love it can drive out your fear (1 John 4:18).

Fullness of the Spirit

We shall explore this subject more fully in the next chapter, but notice here how it's the other secret of overcoming our fears, and the reason is because those who are filled with the Spirit have a new boldness. What a difference there was between the disciples who after Jesus died had *'the doors locked for fear of the Jews'* (John 20:19) and the same people who later *'were all filled with the Holy*

Spirit and spoke the word of God boldly' (Acts 4:31)! While part of that difference can be explained by their confident recognition that Jesus had risen, it was only after Pentecost that they went out fearlessly to preach the gospel and heal the sick. The fullness of the Spirit is one of the main reasons why so many of them were not afraid to face persecution or even die for Jesus.

Thousands of people today who by nature are shy, reticent, nervous or apprehensive, on being filled with the Holy Spirit have become transformed people. One lady, who found it difficult to talk to any stranger in a one-to-one situation, blossomed into a new radiance when in her local house group she frequently spoke words from God. *'Be filled with the Spirit'* (Ephesians 5:18), and overcome fear.

Practical discussion questions

1. Share with one another any particular fears you are conscious of in your life at the moment. Are these easy to overcome?

2. How would you minister to someone diagnosed by a psychiatrist as having a phobia, such as agoraphobia or claustrophobia?

3. How would you minister to a member of your church if someone discerned that he or she had an evil spirit of fear? (2 Timothy 1:7)

4. In the meeting context, in which particular ways can leaders help people to keep their eyes on Jesus and not be distracted?

Question 6: Spirit-filled

Must I Be Filled with the Holy Spirit Before God Can Use Me?

God can use anyone He wishes. He even used King Cyrus, who worshipped other gods, to fulfil His purposes (Isaiah 44:28). And we've already seen how He chose the most unlikely people to be leaders in His Church. Today He uses doctors and therapists who are not Christians to bring healing. So obviously He can use you as a healing channel if you are born of the Spirit (John 3:5).

However, ministering healing without having been baptised in the Holy Spirit can be like trying to smash a huge rock with a hammer compared to destroying the same rock with a stick of dynamite. Or it's like attempting to push a huge bulldozer up a hill with the brake on instead of boarding and using the ignition to start the engine and drive it. *'You will receive power* [dunamis],*'* promised Jesus, **'when the Holy Spirit comes on you'** (Acts 1:8). The difference is in *effectiveness*.

What it is not

Being filled with the Spirit is not the same as other experiences. It is not the same as:

- *regeneration*: you can be a Christian, born again and not be filled
- *consecration*: you can give your all to Christ and not be filled
- *sanctification*: you can lead the holiest life and not be filled
- *feeling*: you can enjoy wonderful feelings and yet not be filled
- *falling*: you can fall under the power of God and not be filled
- *walking in the Spirit*: you can be led and obedient, yet not be filled.

On the other hand, as long as you have been born of the Spirit, you may not have had any of these other experiences, yet you can today be filled with the same Spirit (Acts 2:4; 8:17; 10:44–46; 19:6). For the fullness of the Spirit means you receive *fresh empowering*.

Let's look at some of the differences this can make in healing.

In the words we speak

There is not a single reference in the New Testament where we read of someone or some group being filled with the Holy Spirit without speaking. On every occasion those concerned immediately open their mouths: either to speak *to* God, or *for* God, or to sing. Therefore, while the Spirit also works in many other ways, and sometimes in silence, there is no point in asking to be filled unless we are prepared to open our mouths straightaway. Notice what God did at Pentecost: *'All of them were filled with the Holy Spirit'* (Acts 2:4). And notice what the first Christians did: they *'began to speak in other tongues as the Spirit enabled them.'* Consequently, for those Christians wondering how they will know what to say, 'the dentist's text' seems particularly appropriate here: *'Open wide your mouth and I will fill it'* (Psalm 81:10)!

Witnesses of Christ

Jesus had promised His disciples that once they were baptised in the Spirit, *'you will be my witnesses ... to the ends of the earth'* (Acts 1:8). One of the first ways they boldly witnessed was in healing a lame man (Acts 3:1–16). When they were told to keep quiet about Jesus using them, Peter fearlessly replied, *'we cannot help speaking about what we have seen and heard'* (Acts 4:20).

I was once preparing a girl for confirmation and spoke about the need to be filled with the Spirit if we are to witness boldly. 'Oh, I don't need that!' she exclaimed. 'I already witness to my friends at school.' 'That's great!' I said approvingly. 'But can you say you cannot *help* speaking about what you've seen and heard?' 'No,' she said, taken aback, 'perhaps I *do* need to be filled after all!'

In Samaria,

> *'When the crowds heard Philip and saw the miraculous signs he did, they all paid close attention to what he said.'*   (Acts 8:6)

A clue to his effectiveness is in Acts 6:3–5: he was one of the deacons who were *'full of the Spirit and wisdom'*. When Paul witnessed to Christ in the power of the Spirit it was in three ways: *'by what I have **said** and **done** – by the **power of signs and miracles** ... '* (Romans 15:18–19). People were drawn not only by his words and deeds but by the signs he performed. And today there's no better point of contact for evangelism than healing.

Witnessing of healing

Pauline was a Spirit-filled member of a church where I was vicar. She has long blonde hair, and whenever the Lord referred to her in the gifts of the Spirit He would call her 'the fair maiden'. One day He said to Christine and me, 'Go and visit the fair maiden in her home.' When we arrived, Pauline was very distressed. She was in agony with a trapped nerve in her neck. 'The doctor has just been,' she said, 'and he's given me a prescription for some painkillers. But now the Lord's sent you too, perhaps you'll minister to me.' So, while we prayed for Pauline, Christine laid hands on her neck, just as Jesus used to touch the affected part of a sick person's body (e.g. John 9:6). A few days later when we next saw Pauline she was waving the prescription around enthusiastically. 'I didn't need this!' she said delightedly. Her pains had gone.

For several years afterwards we'd catch sight of Pauline chatting to people in the village street near her home. Opening her purse she would bring out her prescription as evidence of how Jesus had healed her, and would use the opportunity to talk about Him. We need more people like Pauline who use their healing in this way.

In the gifts we share

Natural gifts, such as craftsmanship or artistic ability, may be displayed by any person. And the Lord may bestow functional or ministry gifts, such as pastoring or teaching (Ephesians 4:11), on any Christian. But the supernatural or charismatic (momentary) gifts in 1 Corinthians 12:8–10 are mainly manifested by Spirit-filled believers, and these are passed on to those who need them.

All of these spiritual gifts are invaluable in healing ministry, and later we shall explore some of them more fully, especially in chapters 17–21. Here I shall dwell on the gift of tongues, as it's often the first such gift that a Spirit-filled Christian exhibits.

Speaking in tongues

It is possible to be filled without speaking in tongues, but any believer who speaks in a genuine tongue has been Spirit-filled. This powerful gift has three main functions, along with others:

1. as a sign of a person's baptism in the Holy Spirit (Acts 10:46)
2. as a gift for private prayer and praise (1 Corinthians 14:2)
3. as a message given by God to a Christian for others, in which case it needs interpreting so they understand it (1 Corinthians 14:13).

Frequently the gift of tongues leads to the manifestation of other spiritual gifts. Therefore, in addition to the many benefits it is able to bring, it is worth seeking because of it being a doorway to other abilities that the Lord can bestow on you. Moreover, while some people just find themselves renewed in the Spirit and speaking in tongues when they were not specifically expecting to, others need deliberately to pray and pursue such a release of power so that they can be better equipped for God's service:

'Follow the way of love and eagerly desire spiritual gifts ... '
(1 Corinthians 14:1)

Tongues aid healing

Soon after a clergyman aged seventy-five began regularly praying in tongues people told him he looked twenty years younger. For *'He who speaks in a tongue edifies himself'* (1 Corinthians 14:4).

Jackie Pullinger discovered that when she stopped her habit of regularly praying in tongues things 'stopped happening'. When she prayed thus and encouraged Christian drug addicts to do the same, they found swift freedom without any horrific withdrawal symptoms.

A man who attended one of our residential conferences told me how he had suffered from shoulder pain for several months. He had been to his doctor and osteopath to receive treatment but was no better. Then he decided to ask God to give him the appropriate tongue for his situation, and he soon found himself praying in a language he had not used before. His healing followed, instant and permanent.

But why do we need the public gift of tongues? Why not just the interpretation which everyone can understand? The tongue is like a red traffic light warning us to stop and listen, because God has something important to say. We then wait in silence for the green light of interpretation to follow. Notice that even when Paul is writing to a church which has misused this gift he declares, *'I would like every one of you to speak in tongues'* (1 Corinthians 14:5), and *'do not forbid speaking in tongues'* (1 Corinthians 14:39).

Tongues aid deliverance

'In my name they will drive out demons; they will speak in new tongues ... '   (Mark 16:17)

Sometimes an evil spirit has refused to leave a demonised person when addressed in English but once we have come against it in a tongue it has swiftly made its exit. At one meeting I was ministering to a man with evil spirits when his mother began screaming as the demon in her identified with the ones which were being cast out of her son (cf. Acts 8:7). Chris hastened to deliver her and, speaking in tongues, commanded the demon to leave in a definite tone. Afterwards the two women warmly embraced each other as they rejoiced that Jesus had set the mother free.

In the ways we minister

Paul writes about different kinds of gifts, of ministry, and of the ways Christians minister (1 Corinthians 12:4–6), because God is a God of variety. So some healing ministers major on anointing with oil, some on the Holy Communion, some on words of knowledge, and some like Chris and me on the laying-on-of-hands. God is not restricted to Catholic or Protestant, sacramental or charismatic, high church or low church, traditional churches or new fellowships. He is bigger than them all, and we must not attempt to limit Him.

Command prayers

However, because the fullness of the Holy Spirit results in a new boldness, those who have experienced this are more likely to pray and act in positive, powerful ways. We can use the authority Jesus has delegated to His Church (Matthew 10:1) both to command blessing and rebuke evil. For example, we frequently use command prayers as well as request ones. All the prayers for healing in the New Testament are command prayers except the general one in Acts 4:30 which is a request: *'Stretch . . . out your hand to heal . . . '*

Similarly, we do not just say prayers like 'Lord, make Michael's legs better', but 'Michael, in the name of Jesus walk!' (Acts 3:6). We would only use these particular words when we feel it is right to and when someone is given faith for this, but frequently we end our requests with other command prayers such as, 'Be healed!' or 'Find healing!' We do not require immense faith to pray like this if the person understands that how and when healing happens is up to God. Also, while He does answer many request prayers, perhaps we'll see more happen if we use more prayers of authority.

How it can happen

Christians are filled with the Holy Spirit in all kinds of ways, but being renewed through this experience is often compared with drinking (1 Corinthians 12:13). Drinking is a conscious act, and it is as we appropriate what we have asked for that we find we have received it. When someone seeks this release of power the first time it should be for God's glory and on His terms. But if individuals adhere to the following conditions there is no reason normally why they should not receive the gift and know it. If they do not, it's a matter of trusting and persevering until they do.

1. Become a Christian

If individuals have not already accepted Jesus as their Saviour and Lord they should be encouraged to do so, for *'if anyone does not have the Spirit of Christ, he does not belong to Christ'* (Romans 8:9).

2. Renounce any occult involvement

This is necessary if not already done because *'No one can serve two masters'* (Matthew 6:24), and Satan may use the opportunity to prevent the Christian from enjoying the full release offered. Any known blockages should also be confessed and given over to the Lord, so that the person as far as possible is unrestricted.

3. Be thirsty for the Lord

Jesus is the source:

> ' "If anyone is thirsty, let him come to me and drink. Whoever believes in me ... streams of living water will flow from within him." By this he meant the Spirit ... '   (John 7:37–39)

4. Ask to be filled

Jesus has also assured us:

> ' ... how much more will your Father in heaven give the Holy Spirit to those who ask him!'   (Luke 11:13)

5. Believe the Lord is doing it

> 'And these signs will accompany those who believe: In my name ... they will speak in new tongues ... '   (Mark 16:17)

We can also thank God that He has begun to answer the prayer whether we feel anything or not.

6. Speak out, trusting the Holy Spirit to give words

Remember:

> 'All of them were filled with the Holy Spirit and began to speak in tongues as the Spirit enabled them.'   (Acts 2:4)

7. Having received, keep getting filled

This is the true meaning of Ephesians 5:18: *'be filled with the Spirit'*. When D.L. Moody was asked why he needed so many fillings of the Spirit, he replied, 'I leak!' We can pray to be filled again before opportunities to speak or minister, before difficult tasks, and at the beginning of each day. We should see a real difference.

Practical discussion questions

1. How can healing ministry be restricted if there is no obvious evidence of the Holy Spirit's moving in power? (Acts 4:30–31)

2. Do you know of particular people who have become Christians, or might do, because of their interest in healing (see Acts 8:6)?

3. Someone wishes to be filled with the Holy Spirit but does not wish to speak in tongues. How would you encourage and help her or him?

4. In what ways are you using the authority that Jesus has given to you? When might your church expect to use command prayers?

SECTION 3

How?

Question 7: Self-confidence
Do Some People Get Better as a Result of Placebo, or Suggestion?

Certainly some do, and this question is significant because these days some Christians are asking how healing happens. When Chris and I first encountered Christian healing we were not concerned to discover how it worked in natural and scientific terms. We were moving in the realm of faith and the supernatural, and were simply thrilled that God was healing so many sick people through prayer.

Does it matter?

It's still not essential to explain how healing happens for people to accept and experience it. But it helps if we at least know some answers so that we can more intelligently help the following:

1. those people, especially in the medical and scientific worlds, who will only accept things demonstrated to their satisfaction
2. those who are sceptical about any spiritual explanations of the results of healing ministry, and only accept natural ones
3. those Christians who remain suspicious of conveyors of healing like complementary therapists, and who are under the impression that a spiritual power other than God's is behind their work. (This is particularly relevant for the purpose of this book.)

The question also raises the issue of self-confidence, so I believe it is an important one to answer.

The middle verse of the whole Bible, Psalm 118:8, states:

> *'It is better to take refuge in the* Lord
>   *than to trust in man.'*

Some have used this verse to argue that we should not have any confidence in ourselves, but it does not say that. My own experience is that for effective healing, while first we must trust God, to a certain extent we also have to trust ourselves and those who help us.

The power of the mind

While Christians discourage the development of such practices as clairvoyance and telepathy, we recognise that the human mind has tremendous power, and we've still not discovered all its potential.

Intuitive gifts

Some people have intuitive gifts that extend beyond the normal realm of the senses. Christine may be thinking about someone, and the next moment the telephone will ring and it's the person she has been thinking about who has contacted her. She has such an ability not because she's a Christian. It's psychic, but not in the sense that spiritists mean. It's undoubtedly an ability from God.

Positive thinking

The best psychiatrists encourage the use of positive thinking. Just as the attitudes of the mind can cause illness in the body, so the mind can be a major factor in helping the body to recover. We have found that negative thoughts and attitudes, as well as negative words, tend to restrict healing. If I visit a seriously ill person in hospital and I'm thinking, 'She probably won't pull through', my attitude could speed her deterioration. If instead I approach her with a positive outlook it can aid her improvement.

When ministering, Chris and I have sought to picture the sufferer in a healthy condition – for example, the crippled walking, the blind seeing, the depressed laughing – while praying positively, specifically and expectantly, though without giving false hopes. If Christians get into the habit of thinking positively they will automatically pray positively and see positive results. If we pray with a negative outlook, people are likely to see us, but if we pray with a positive attitude they are more likely to see Jesus.

The place of suggestion

When other people suggest things to us, or when we consciously or unconsciously suggest things to ourselves (auto-suggestion), these thoughts play a part towards our healing, though they vary in the extent to which they affect us and they are, of course, fallible.

Mind over matter

Christians would not normally attempt deliberately to influence healing purely by exercising mind over matter, neither can all healing be explained in these terms. Some of us have experienced too many 'coincidences' in answer to our prayers (Mark 11:24)! We also have to be especially discerning about treatment such as hypnotherapy, where suggestion appears to play a prominent role. However, our minds, with all their wealth of information and their preconceived ideas, are bound to influence the way we proceed.

Sharing needs

Some ministers at healing services discourage sufferers from mentioning their needs. One reason given is that suggestion may play too large a part in the ministry, for such ministers tend to view this as a threat rather than an ally. They argue that God already knows the need, or that He may reveal it to them, and also that the person may go on talking too much. In addition, they may lay hands on people and anoint with oil in silence, rather than praying aloud.

All these things can be right under some circumstances but most healing ministers encourage sufferers to mention at least one major need that concerns them. While it is the Lord who does the healing, we believe He wants to make use of the things that people share, the questions we ask them, the gifts we may manifest and the experience that we have gained on previous occasions.

The placebo effect

The placebo effect is defined as a positive therapeutic effect claimed by a patient after receiving a placebo (an inactive drug or a sham therapy) believed by the patient to be an active drug. One third of all people, given an inactive compound to relieve a particular symptom, will report some relief from that symptom.

Response to a placebo may be different according to the way that the drug is presented, such as through tablets or injections. One study showed that red placebo tablets were more effective in relieving pain than blue ones were, and blue ones more than green.

The double blind trial

These days the orthodox medical doctor is taught that all the new knowledge about drugs or medical techniques must pass through the 'double blind placebo controlled trial'. In this everything must be tested in such a way that neither participants nor researchers know if they are taking the real thing or a dummy (placebo). Much thought and energy and enormous amounts of money are poured into testing the drugs, and all doctors are taught to discount any drug that fails the trial as a result of the placebo effect.

In the 1980s orthodox medicine, based on scientific rationalism, dismissed virtually all the natural therapies as placebo effect. And there is still hesitancy among some doctors to accept any form of medicine that is not purely physical, including Christian healing. They will not recognise any complementary therapies until they have passed the double blind trials and proved not to result from placebo effect. But the climate of opinion has been gradually changing, especially in view of the fact that one in three people in the UK regularly visits an alternative therapist of some kind.

In response to Question 11 we'll consider some of the scientific evidence for the validity of such therapies, but one problem is they cannot all be tested through the double blind trial because many of them are completely different forms of medicine. They do not match remedies purely to diseases but to someone's overall needs. This does not mean, however, that they can easily be dismissed as the result of placebo, and sometimes they *can* be tested in the orthodox manner. The double-blind trial was used with some success to demonstrate the effectiveness of homoeopathic remedies over placebo, such as in the use of potentised pollens for treating hay fever patients.

Children

Some complementary therapies, such as homoeopathy, have had a good deal of success among children and unconscious people, and all of this cannot easily be explained as simply due to placebo effect. Alan Crook, in *A Christian's Guide to Homeopathy* (p. 35) describes how in 1994 the American journal *Paediatrics* published research about homoeopathic treatment of acute childhood diarrhoea in Nicaragua. The group treated with homoeopathic medicines recovered up to 25 per cent more rapidly than the group using placebos.

Animals
Homoeopathy has also had much success in treating animals, according to data held by leading practitioners. One significant venture in South America demonstrated how many more animals recovered from a serious disease after treatment using homoeopathic remedies than those treated with allopathic drugs.

Plants
Plant growth cannot easily be explained by placebo either. According to an article by Sally Hammond entitled *We Are All Healers*, Rev. Franklin Loehr has described controlled experiments in which the growth rate of plants was speeded up to 20 per cent by the systematic prayer of individuals and groups of people. They had also visualised every test plant thriving in an ideal setting.

The prayer of faith

James assures us, *'the prayer offered in faith will make the sick person well'* (James 5:15). So it is this, rather than the prayer of hope, that triumphs. Non-Christian doctors may view prayer as a useful prop for patients who need something to believe in. To them it may be a form of placebo that sometimes brings results. To the believer it is much more. A young man called Howard was diagnosed with a life-threatening obstruction in his neck and was given five years to live. Howard was not then a Christian, but he had confidence that if only I could touch him he would be healed (cf. Mark 5:28). He travelled 250 miles from Huddersfield to Tunbridge Wells, to a Breath healing meeting at St James' Church. There we ministered to him in Jesus' name. Soon afterwards he was given an ultrasound test at a Huddersfield hospital, which would normally have taken a few minutes, but it took fifty-five minutes before the medics would accept that there was no sign of Howard's problem!

Did mind over matter play a part in Howard's sudden restoration? Perhaps it did. He certainly had self-confidence. But after the result he became a Christian and gave Jesus the praise, because however it had happened, he knew who was ultimately responsible.

Practical discussion questions

1. How would you minister to a Christian person who is lacking in self-confidence and who also has an inferiority complex?

2. The Lord Jesus Christ is a positive thinker. How was this demonstrated in His earthly ministry? (e.g. Matthew 21:18–22)

3. Do you think every treatment should be scientifically tested?

4. What 'coincidences' have you and your fellowship experienced in response to prayer? Are you expecting more? (Mark 11:24)

Question 8: Therapeutic Touch

May We Touch the Sick for Healing Without Praying for Them?

In *It Hurts to Heal* Chris and I described how during the 1970s the first properly controlled experiments were conducted in America into healing through touch. These were led by Bernard Grad, whose pioneering work is referred to by Dan Benor in *Healing Research* Volume 1 (pp. 182–183). One of these experiments was with three groups of mice consisting of twenty-five in each group and with identical induced wounds on their backs. The first group was left to heal naturally; the second was given healing through touch; and the third was subjected to a lamp simulating exactly the amount of heat given off by the healer's hands. Each group's healing rate was carefully monitored. The twenty-five mice that had received healing through touch made dramatically faster recoveries than those in the other two groups. Touch aids healing. This means that many people are being healed through touch without always being prayed for. And we are all aware, too, of the benefit received by a baby from its mother's touch, by a patient from the nurse's touch, and by a bereaved person from the touch of a friend.

To pray or not to pray?

When Christine was first called to train as an osteopath, some Christians asked her, 'Why do you need to do that, when you already have such a powerful ministry of laying-on-of-hands with prayer?' They did not instantly appreciate that God could use her in both. Should Christians touch for healing without praying? Sometimes. In healing ministry it's usual to include both the touch, through laying-on-of-hands and perhaps anointing, and the prayer, through at least one person who is ministering praying audibly. In other contexts, such as the therapist's clinic, touch is given without prayer, often by a non-Christian, yet healing can still be from God. Let's explore in detail the value of these two methods of healing.

Touching with prayer

The giving of communion and the ministry of anointing with oil bring churchgoers into close contact with their leaders, which may involve touch. The sharing of God's peace is frequently expressed through handshakes and hugs. But it's primarily through laying-on-of-hands that Jesus' healing touch is bestowed in the context of prayer: *'laying his hands on each one, he healed them'* (Luke 4:40).

Laying-on-of-hands in the Bible
In the Scriptures laying-on-of-hands is used in connection with penitence (Leviticus 16:21), with assurance (Revelation 1:17), healing (Mark 16:18), receiving the Holy Spirit (Acts 8:17), ordaining and commissioning (Acts 13:3), and specific blessing (Mark 10:16). When Jesus laid hands on the children we can be sure the blessing received by any sick among them was healing.

Make it available
We have seen in previous chapters how, when Christians give and receive the touch of Jesus rightly, something always happens. This does not mean we are to force it on people, for the Bible says, *'Do not be hasty in the laying on of hands'* (1 Timothy 5:22), but we are to make it available. One church decided they'd have no meeting from which someone who was sick or in pain would have to go away without the opportunity of receiving this ministry, for the writer to the Hebrews classes laying-on-of-hands among the basic foundations and doctrines of the Church (Hebrews 6:1–2). Coming forward for this ministry can also be an excellent way of responding to God's word and showing we mean business with Him.

Make it known

So can sharing about it. Some years ago I spoke about healing at the annual meeting of the Baptist deacons in the Huddersfield area. As a result Chris and I, with a team from our own church, were invited to lead healing services in several Baptist chapels. At the end of one of these meetings an elderly lady clutching a stick mentioned that she had been too shy to come forward for the laying-on-of-hands. When I asked if she would like us to pray for her in the vestry she gladly agreed. We ministered to her there for the spinal trouble, from which she had suffered for some years.

The next Saturday we took some of our own church members to a Praise, Healing and Renewal rally in Halifax. There a woman stood up to testify and we suddenly realised that she was sharing about the elderly lady with the stick. 'Everybody's talking about it in the shops,' she was saying, 'for everybody in the village knows her. Her pain has gone and she doesn't need her stick any more.'

Precious and normal

In some churches laying-on-of-hands is taken for granted so much that it loses its preciousness and power. In other churches it is so special that it is only offered occasionally. It should be both precious and normal: precious as it once was to the man born blind (John 9:25), yet normal as it was to Jesus. It was so natural for Him to touch people, not just at arranged gatherings but whenever in His compassion He recognised their needs (Matthew 14:14). And it's worth remembering His touch can mean not just our hands on the head of those who are sick but perhaps on their shoulder, the affected part of their body, an arm wrapped around them, or simply holding their hand.

The affected part

The particular value of touching the affected part of a person's body when we pray (John 9:6) is that the healing energy can soak in at that point, though God's blessing is not just for that part but for the whole body and personality. When we laid hands on one woman's neck she felt it loosen immediately. 'Now I can obey that command,' she joked. ' *"Speak not with a stiff neck"* [Psalm 75:5, AV].' Sometimes Christians have laid hands on the affected parts of animals and machines as well as people, frequently with encouraging results.

Prayer by proxy

There is no doubt that ministry is most effective when it's given directly to the person in his or her presence. The four friends who brought a paralysed man for healing recognised the value of this when, because of the great crowds, they could not get into Peter's house where Jesus was living at Capernaum (the site of which we've visited, as it's been unearthed and evidenced by archaeologists). So they pushed through the crowd, mounted the flat roof, made a hole in it, and lowered the man to the feet of Jesus (Mark 2:3–4).

But Christian healing can also take place by proxy, as it did when the centurion came to ask Jesus to heal his servant, who was sick at home (Matthew 8:5–13). And this may happen through laying-on-of-hands with prayer. Large cysts had appeared in one lady's breasts at Barking, Essex, and she was waiting for surgery. At one of our Woodford meetings this lady's mother received laying-on-of-hands for her. Almost overnight the lumps disappeared, and at a hospital check-up three months after this there was still no sign of them.

Soaking prayer

Many people need a second touch, like the blind man Jesus healed, who first saw people like trees walking (Mark 8:22–26). And some need regular sessions. When a person shows signs of improvement after one or two sessions of laying-on-of-hands we've often found it beneficial to provide soaking prayer, which is usually a course of treatment in relaxed surroundings. We've kept our hands on the affected part of the sufferer's body for long periods of time – say twenty to thirty minutes – while praying, worshipping in song, or talking informally. The energy flows through him or her via the point of contact.

Soaking prayer may also take place in one session where required. Andrew was a young man from Huddersfield who was knocked down by a motorcycle on his way home from a disco. He was hurriedly taken to Pinderfields Hospital at Wakefield, suffering from a fractured skull. The doctors told Andrew's parents, 'We don't expect him to last the night.' But they let me in to see him as I was wearing my clerical 'ring of confidence'. I laid hands on his unconscious body while picturing him whole, and prayed in tongues for half an hour. Others were praying too. Andrew was conscious after five days and back in our street doing his paper round within three weeks!

Touching without prayer

There have been some occasions where we have had no opportunity or time to pray. When Chris worked part time in a greengrocer's shop she placed her hand on the manageress's back without saying anything. The manageress later told another shop assistant how her pain had disappeared. But Chris only kept quiet because the shop was busy with customers and she had not yet had much opportunity there to talk about the Lord. When possible we do not want people just to find they are healed but to know it is God who has done it.

Touch in osteopathy

However, prayer is not often possible or appropriate when people are receiving therapy. Yet the touch is an important part of some therapies, and God uses the skills and expertise of the therapists to speed healing just as He uses those of doctors, consultants, psychiatrists and nurses, whether or not these are Christians.

The Lord calls Christine's work in osteopathy a ministry, but she is so absorbed in her work when treating patients that she is not usually able to pray at the same time, nor to speak of her faith unless specifically questioned about it. However, her Christian witness shines through all she does, and sometimes she recommends prayer ministry to patients who are ready to benefit from this, as well as suggesting osteopathy to some who come to us for prayer.

Osteopaths do not just treat people for back pain but they work towards the optimum structural integrity unique to each patient. That means they may treat people for anything to do with bones and muscles: shoulder pain, tennis elbow, whiplash, sciatica, pelvic injury and a host of other things, along with dealing with the root causes by looking at the patient's whole body and lifestyle.

Christine has had a complete medical and osteopathic training. She mainly uses soft tissue work (deep massage), articulation, spontaneous release techniques and some manipulation, not only to relieve pain and cure ills but also to help prevent further problems. With babies she also uses cranial techniques, involving sensitive detection of the flow of spinal fluid. The Lord has so made our bodies that, when given the right environment, they can be helped to some extent to heal themselves (cf. Ephesians 4:16).

Touch in other therapies

Reflexology is another therapy where touch is a vital part of the treatment. Reflexes in the feet react to stimulation as their tiny network of nerves are indirectly connected to specific organs and muscles throughout the body. Massage and manipulation of specific points on the feet direct vital energy to the organs needing it. Among the reflexologists are many Christians who do it for Jesus.

Many aromatherapists are Christians too. Touch is used in their treatment as well, since gentle massage is one of the main ways in which the aromatic oils are applied. Often this is therapeutic rather than bringing about complete cure, for example in hospices, where it is frequently an important part of palliative care. But it also aids health and fitness, and so contributes to healing.

Chris and I have an autistic grandson, Daniel. He stopped speaking at eighteen months and it was not until he was five, when my wife had raised the money required, that we were able to take him for Dolphin Human Therapy at Key Largo, Florida. But following this he began speaking some words again, started responding to commands, and was much calmer. We do not know whether the therapists who helped him were Christians, but we do know touch played a part.

In many of the following chapters we shall be exploring the ways in which Christians can relate to therapies, and the concerns that naturally arise about different forms of 'spiritual healing'. We have received hundreds of enquiries asking us to explain what is helpful and what is questionable in this field. People need to know how to discern where the enemy is at work (1 Peter 5:8), but not at the expense of 'throwing out the baby with the bath water'. Here I simply emphasise that where touch is given to aid healing, with or without prayer, if the right people give it in the right manner, it can be of God and therefore it can be the touch of Jesus.

When touch was sufficient

One more instance of the value of touch comes from the days when I was ministering at Trevor Dearing's church, St Paul's, Hainault. Sometimes the spoken word is unintelligible to the needy person, as in the case of a mentally retarded boy brought to me by his parents. Although he could not follow my words he could feel my touch. Twelve months later, when I unexpectedly met the boy's parents at another service, in Ilford, they told me how their son had so improved that he had just taken his GCE exams!

Practical discussion questions

1. List as many ways you can of how to bring the touch of Jesus to people that you know of who are sick or in particular need.

2. What are the advantages and disadvantages of having laying-on-of-hands (1) after the sermon, (2) during the prayers, (3) during the communion, (4) at the close of the service, (5) afterwards?

3. What are the best ways and times for ministering laying-on-of-hands to the children associated with your church? (Mark 10:16)

4. How can your church publicise its healing ministry? Why should people want to come to it rather than a spiritualist church?

Question 9: Meditating Rightly

Which Kinds of Meditation Do You Encourage and Discourage?

Someone has said that *meditation* can be just as effective a cure for some conditions as *medication*. Since the mid-twentieth century a good deal of evidence has backed up this claim. Meditation is not just a passing attraction, as it seemed to be for some when the Beatles went to their guru, the Maharishi. It is another means by which we can be helped towards health, fitness and relaxation, and many people regard it as an effective complementary therapy.

But Christians are not only curious about whether it's effective but whether it's excellent in God's sight, not only if it's real but if it's right, not only if it works but if it's worthy of Him. So the question deserves an answer: we encourage scriptural and contemplative meditation but discourage transcendental meditation.

Scriptural meditation

I have selected over the years forty promises of healing to claim from the Scriptures. One of these is Proverbs 4:20 and 22:

> *'My son . . .*
> *   listen closely to my words . . .*
> *for they are life to those who find them*
> *   and health to a man's whole body.'*

Inwardly digesting

In the old Church of England prayer for Bible Sunday we accept the Scriptures as the word of God written for our learning. We then pray that we may read, mark, learn and inwardly digest them. Reading them is self-explanatory. Marking them is to study them, perhaps with the aid of a concordance, commentary or Bible reading notes. Learning them is valuable:

> *'I have hidden your word in my heart*
> *that I might not sin against you.'*　　　　　(Psalm 119:11)

But it's the inwardly digesting that best describes what meditation means. The cow chews the cud over and over again, and this is necessary if it is to produce the dairy products extracted from it, which we so appreciate. And a characteristic of all kinds of meditation is that we let what we are meditating on sink into our hearts, over and over again.

Communion with God

David wanted the meditation of his heart to be acceptable to God (Psalm 19:14), and scriptural meditation is an exercise of the heart, not just the mind and brain as studying can be. For in it we seek to go beyond the written word to have communion with God.

This meditation is something we do individually, though it may be at a retreat. A quiet place is essential, free from interruption – perhaps a church building, or the quietest room in one's home. It may mean setting aside a time at the beginning or end of the day, for it involves listening to God at a deep level (Psalm 46:10). We can prepare ourselves to meditate by offering the session to God in worship and prayer. Some people find it helpful to have on hand devotional books, such as hymn books and prayer books, to add to what is gained from immersing themselves in the Scriptures. If during the session our thoughts wander we can bring them back gently by recollecting what we've already digested from the Lord.

Supernatural strength

When Christians are ill, fearful or depressed, but not yet to the extent that they cannot relax at all, if they can meditate on the Scriptures their spirits will be fed and they can find healing.

> *'For thus said the Lord ... In returning to Me and resting in Me you
> shall be saved* [healed, delivered, made whole]; *in quietness and
> in (trusting) confidence shall be your strength.'*
>
> (Isaiah 30:15, Amplified Version)

The weak can be given supernatural strength. And they can claim
promises like Joshua 1:8:

> *'Meditate on it* [this book] *day and night ... Then you will be
> prosperous and successful.'*

Use your imagination

Trevor Dearing says that the most important factor in Christian
meditation is our sanctified imagination. Once we have chosen
the subject from the Bible we can begin to imagine in detail what it
involves, remembering that the Lord wishes to speak to each of us
through it, and allow Him with expectancy to make it part of us.

If we are not sure what to meditate on we can ask God to show
us, but it will probably be chosen from one of these four
categories:

1. *A verse.* A favourite is Philippians 4:13:

   > *'I can do everything through him who gives me strength.'*

   There is plenty to dwell on if we take each word in this verse
   at a time, and the last four words all together.

2. *A passage.* Psalm 103, a song of praise for God's blessings and
   compassion, is full of truths to chew over while we let His love
   sink into us.

3. *A scene.* If you have been to the Holy Land you will find
   biblical scenes light up to you more vividly. An example is the
   Pool of Bethesda (John 5:1–15), which is another proven site,
   since its five covered colonnades have been identified.
   Imagine you are standing on the banks above the pool.
   Visualise the blind, lame and paralysed people. Picture the
   invalid unable to get down into the pool while others do.
   Imagine Jesus speaking, curing him, and then slipping away
   quietly.

4. *The Lord.* We can meditate on some aspect of Jesus' character
   or work, such as His name, His beauty, His tenderness,
   sufferings, or victory.

Contemplative meditation

While in scriptural meditation we commune with God in our hearts, our minds are being constantly exercised as we think deeply about what we are meditating on. In contemplative meditation, also known as contemplative prayer, which is especially but not exclusively practised in Catholic circles, the mind is 'put into neutral', and the whole emphasis is on communing with God in our spirits.

Specifically Christian
In this respect it is more like Eastern meditation than that which we have so far described. That does not make it wrong for Christians to practise it, any more than it is wrong for oriental believers to worship Jesus in a manner that is different from the way we worship in our own country. While the *form* is unfamiliar to some, the *content* is specifically Christian. And the healing that sometimes results is from the Lord.

> 'But seek ye first the kingdom of God, and his righteousness; and all these things shall be added unto you.'　　　(Matthew 6:33, AV)

The *'all these things'* Jesus promised include healing. So whenever those meditating seek God's rule in their hearts they are in tune with His will, and can expect to receive His blessings.

Christian mantras
Contemplative meditation in the last few decades has adopted the use of mantras, which originated in Hindhu and Buddhist scriptures, as a means of concentrating on the Lord. A mantra is a word or short phrase or sentence on which the person meditates, while allowing his or her body to relax – every part from the head downwards – and his or her spirit to be available to God. Some people have quiet music playing in the background, while others maintain silence apart from the frequent repetition of the mantra.

A popular Christian mantra is 'Jesus is Lord'. Another might be 'The Lord is my Shepherd'. By only repeating these simple phrases people are able to relax to such an extent that they sometimes 'rest in the Spirit', in the sense of being on a different level of consciousness while they commune with God, and this can be a refreshing experience. We shall explore it more in chapter 33.

Transcendental meditation (TM)

Many people now use this term to mean simple meditation as part of relaxation techniques. For example, they may be encouraged to visualise a particular scene such as a beautiful seaside setting or glorious sunset. Christians need have no problem with this, in fact we would all probably benefit from it from time to time.

Eastern religions

But proper TM is very different from this sort of meditation. It involves concepts of Eastern religions that are at variance with Christianity. The real world is viewed as an 'illusion', and participants are encouraged to withdraw their consciousness from this, going beyond normal thought to make contact with the underlying reality of life. The 'Absolute' on which they meditate is non-personal, for they 'progress' to a realisation that god is non-personal energy.

Transcendental meditation is also more associated with humanistic concepts than Christian ones. In humanism and secularism emphasis is on changing society through education, ethics and enlightenment without the necessity of true religion. In TM, and also in the New Age movement which endorses it, enlightenment is a major aim, but gained through separating the soul from the body. 'Knowledge', it is believed, comes through control of the mind and thoughts, and in this way we can achieve a fuller union with 'ultimate reality'.

These ideas are not too dissimilar from the Gnostic heresies of the early Christian Church. How different is the Christian's aim!

> 'Now this is eternal life: that they may know you, the only true God, and Jesus Christ, whom you have sent.' (John 17:3)

We know a God who is personal, through entering into a relationship with His Son.

Better ways

Whenever Christians meditate they must be happy that what they are meditating on is right and good (Philippians 4:8), and they should never deliberately allow their minds to go blank. Some people, through practices like transcendental meditation, have unwittingly become captives of Satan, as Paul foretold they would (1 Timothy 4:1).

But we do not need to follow their example when there are so many better ways for us to find healing and wholeness, and when we have Jesus Himself to think upon. Even when we are not able to stop to meditate we may be surprised by a fresh revelation of Himself to us. One lady who was not a Christian was painting a picture of our Lord on the cross. As she did she was conscious of a Presence near her, and she wept as she was convicted that she too was to blame for His hanging there. Her life was transformed from that moment.

Practical discussion questions

1. What insights have you gained from meditating on a particular aspect of Scripture? Has this experience changed you inside?

2. Choose one of the promises of healing in the Bible and claim it for someone your group knows who is sick or in need.

3. Why do you think silence and quiet music can be conducive to an effective period of contemplative meditation? (Psalm 37:7)

4. A friend is seeking reality and wants to try transcendental meditation. How would you encourage him or her to try Jesus instead?

SECTION 4

Endorsement

Question 10: Orthodox Medicine
How Far Can We Rely on Orthodox Medicine to Solve Our Problems?

I've always remembered a significant comment made by our doctor in Hailsham, East Sussex, when I'd just begun my parish ministry: 'You know, nine out of ten of my patients should come to *you!*' He had come to the conclusion that many problems, which appear to be of the body, are also problems of the mind and the spirit.

Doctors are often only too well aware of the complex nature of people's problems, that many of these are not purely physical, and that their particular skills and expertise in assisting our bodies to heal can only take us so far in our quest for wholeness. But we thank God for the medical profession, for often in spite of difficult conditions and long hours they are doing great work.

Jesus approved of doctors. He once said, *'It is not the healthy who need a doctor but the sick'* (Mark 2:17). Of course doctors at that time were often more like some of the natural therapists of today, and there were a number of occult healers and sorcerers who claimed to be physicians. But He upheld the value of doctors.

Privileges of the medical profession

There are still many benefits available in our health service.

Dedication
With notable exceptions – a number of high-profile cases have been documented in the media – there are thousands of doctors, nurses, consultants and specialists who are dedicated to caring for the sick and helping them to recover. Many of these view the patient as more important than the treatment, and 'First do no harm' is not a meaningless phrase to them. We can still trust them to do all that they can for us to the best of their ability.

Many of us will also benefit from the advances in modern medical science. Recently new remedies to treat and slow down AIDS, breast cancer and Alzheimer's disease have been discovered, especially in the realm of genetics. Diseases which not many years ago were life threatening are treatable, and many people are living longer as a consequence.

Confirmation

One of the doctor's qualifications which especially relates to Christian healing is the ability to confirm when a cure has taken place. When a leper was cleansed Jesus told him, *'go, show yourself to the priest'* (Matthew 8:4), but today it is medical doctors and consultants that perform the function of confirmation. When the illness is serious we advise the sufferer not to announce that he or she is completely healed until this has been medically confirmed.

Heather, who lives at Crawley, West Sussex, was diagnosed as having stomach cancer. After we ministered to her the tumour in her stomach shrank from the size of a tennis ball to that of a table tennis ball. After further ministry the tumour disappeared completely, so that at first the hospital authorities thought they were looking at someone else's X-rays! But the cure was confirmed.

Salvation

Many Christian doctors and nurses have been involved with Breath, and it's always a joy to be asked to lay hands on them so that they can be equipped by the Lord for their daily tasks. Burrswood is a Christian healing centre that provides both medical care and a range of healthcare facilities, such as counselling, osteopathy and physiotherapy. Christian people in medicine are at the sharp end of putting into practice our Lord's command to heal the sick.

Problems of the medical profession

In addition to the general conditions and financial constraints which characterise our health service, other considerations are relevant.

Consultations

The GP has generally only a few minutes in which to diagnose and begin treating the patient. This is one of the many reasons why people are sometimes visiting complementary therapists, for these (at a price) can usually give much more time. For the same reason the GP sometimes resorts to a trial and error approach in making his or her diagnosis, and perhaps will not make so much use of touch.

While doctors may give excellent advice and treatment when it comes to acute illness, they are sometimes unable to help patients with a chronic condition as much as they would like to, whereas therapists can often help to enhance their quality of life.

Perhaps the primary difference between orthodox medical treatment and complementary therapy, however, is that the former is usually reductionist and the latter holistic. The heart specialist is no doubt excellent at treating the heart, but perhaps nothing else. The osteopath treats not just the presenting problem, such as neck trouble, but the whole person. A greater number of medics are now seeking to be more holistic, but have not usually been trained to do it that way.

Medications

The type of treatment given by therapists is also quite different from the drugs prescribed by the medical doctor and the surgery performed by the consultant. Complementary remedies are normally non-toxic, non-invasive and non-suppressant. Treatment is aimed primarily at building up health rather than eradicating disease. Health is viewed as the complete well-being of the person treated.

Generally treatment has no side-effects. Medical drugs are often a help and may be essential, but side-effects are sometimes calamitous. Iatrogenic disease is that which results from medical treatment: damage from prescribed drugs, wrong diagnosis or other mistakes. Globally 106,000 people die every year from prescription drugs – 40,000 in Britain, where 2.2 million patients are hospitalised or incapacitated by such drugs. Christians are naturally concerned.

Limitations

Over 90 per cent of the world's population still have no easy access to orthodox Western medicine, so will have to rely on other forms of treatment. While wonderfully surgeons can use television to direct operations performed miles away, a number of operations and invasive techniques are controversial or appear unnecessary.

In spite of the very rigorous tests that we've already noted are carried out on drugs, in 1991 a British Medical Association report said that 85 per cent of medical treatments remained untested or unproven. Conversely, while many Christians are glad when there is evidence for the value of helpful remedies, having scientifically to demonstrate something before accepting its value can sometimes be a barrier to exercising faith (cf. Thomas – John 20:25).

Prayer and the medical profession

So we praise God for the privileges and pray about the problems.

Combinations

Chris and I have often known people healed through a combination of prayer and medicine. A lady was shown by God that a woman with cancer would be healed through this combination. Others thought she had no hope, but, after the woman was wonderfully restored, the Christian lady was able to witness about this in the hospital.

But notice briefly some misunderstandings that we've encountered:

1. *'I would rather go to the Lord than the doctor.'*
   When we ministered to a mentally ill woman at Erith, North Kent, then recommended that she see a psychiatrist, she refused, saying, 'I want the *Lord* to heal me.' Only when we told her the Lord could work through psychiatrists as well as through prayer did she go to the psychiatrist. She was much better very quickly afterwards.

2. *'Healing should only be done in the name of Jesus.'*
   While Christians minister only in that name, medical practitioners who do not do it for Jesus can just as much be agents of healing.

3. *'It is lack of faith to keep going to the doctor after prayer.'*
   On the contrary, visiting the doctor may be a way of putting our faith into action. We've already seen that more ministry may be necessary before complete healing results. So may more medicine.

4. *'Now I've had prayer I'm going to stop all my drugs at once.'*
   This could be dangerous. It's usually best to come off gradually, preferably with the doctor's consent, though there are exceptions.

Explanations

We should not be surprised if the doctor responds cautiously to us if we report a healing as an answer to prayer, even if that doctor is a Christian. Doctors' medical training tells them that this may not be complete cure but alleviation of symptoms, remission, spontaneous restoration, or that a wrong diagnosis has been made.

However, any of these opinions can be used as an excuse for not accepting another explanation, that God has been at work in other ways. When we believe someone's healing from serious illness is partly the result of prayer, the wisest course is to share the facts and let the doctor make up his or her own mind about it.

Transformations

However ill someone may be, God can do the impossible (Mark 10:27). Many doctors and surgeons do all they can for their patients in the context of their own work and skills, but some Christian medics also go out of their way to seek help elsewhere when they can do little more themselves. One such was a doctor in Essex who had a patient with terminal cancer. Recognising that God could do what he could not, he came on behalf of his patient to receive laying-on-of-hands for him. Instantly there was improvement in the man's condition, and he was able to go back to work within a fortnight. Over a long period the patient continued to receive both medicine and ministry, and after several years he was confirmed as clear.

Prayer can help those making life and death decisions. When I was Curate at Buckhurst Hill in Essex, we prayed for eleven-week-old Rebecca, seriously ill with circulatory problems. After a crucial four-hour heart operation she was restored safely to her parents. The local press described this as a 'miracle cure', but our rector, Peter, told them, 'We asked God to guide the hand of the surgeon. I believe we have created the right spiritual environment for the child to recover in.' Doctor Jesus had been put in charge.

Practical discussion questions

1. How might someone bring the ministry of laying-on-of-hands and anointing with oil to a patient in a hospital bed? (Psalm 41:3)

2. How can a Christian nurse best serve Jesus in her or his daily work?

3. Have you encountered any misunderstandings about how God works through medicine? How would you seek to correct these?

4. What differences would it make for Christian healing and other therapies in the UK to be under the National Health Service?

Question 11: **Scientific Proof**
What Evidence Is There that Therapies Are Scientifically Valid?

Vast numbers of Christians now accept the thousands of healings in the Church's ministry without their being proved, and I do not believe we must wait for total proof before using other therapies. But if we are to trust therapists to treat us, we must be sure as far as possible that remedies they give to us are safe and sound. In recent years there are signs that therapists have accepted the need for relevant research and regulation. Many doctors, sometimes disenchanted with medicine and impressed by results of therapies, have collaborated with the therapists to undertake sound research. Even the treatment of cancer, which is far more than the tumour, can be greatly enhanced by the use of complementary therapies, as Bernie Siegel, who is an American oncologist, has demonstrated.

The results of research

Healthy foods
What orthodox doctors once often rejected is now sometimes incorporated into their recommendations, as either remedies have been demonstrated to their satisfaction or there is such a demand for something considered beneficial that it has been adopted. One example is doctors advising patients to take fish oil and garlic to help to prevent heart attacks. This idea originally came from complementary medicine. Another is folic acid, now recommended by the Department of Health for pregnant women to help prevent them having babies with spina bifida. Nutritional therapists had been recommending this for years. Hyperactive disruptive children have been shown to be greatly helped by not eating artificial additives and junk foods. Many nutritional aids are scientifically attested.

Energy medicine

Homoeopathy is regarded as an energy medicine, since its remedies act as a trigger for releasing energy to speed healing. We shall
explore them more in chapter 23, but think about one instance
now. During 1854 there was a cholera epidemic in London. The
treatment statistics from the various London hospitals disclosed
that over 50 per cent of cholera patients had died during this
epidemic. But there was one exception. The London Homoeopathic Hospital revealed that only 16.4 per cent of its patients
with cholera had died.

Acupuncture is another of the energy medicines. A number of
studies have evaluated its use in the UK, Europe and China, and
recorded objective physiological effects. The chief result was a
diminished awareness of pain, such as migraine. Another study
was made of the use of electroacupuncture, in which the normal
acupuncture needles are connected to an electric current after
insertion. The result was that treatment of fibromyalgia produced
significant benefit.

Doctors often find it hard to accept the validity of acupuncture
as energy medicine because it does not conform to their ideas
of physiology. Many will accept acupuncture as useful, especially
for reducing pain, but on the grounds that pain-killing endomorphins are released in it. This release is certainly one of its
effects. But here I am indebted to the Christian nutritionist Rachel
Temple for her treatise *Medicine – The Christian Dilemma*. She
describes how Dr Robert Becker, who has spent his life investigat-
ing the electromagnetic properties of living things, has found
specific, reproducible and significant electrical activity at each of
many acupuncture points that he has tested. He has further
demonstrated that meridians – those channels of energy that are
identified in therapies such as acupuncture and reflexology – have
the electrical characteristics of transmission lines, such as would
be required.

And Rachel Temple explains how two doctors in Paris suc-
ceeded in visualising different meridians by injecting a radioactive
tracer at an acupuncture point and, by using a gamma ray camera,
found that the radioactivity travelled along the meridian at a
velocity of 3–5 centimetres per minute. This accords with the
Chinese claim of 25 circulations per day. The rate was slower in
diseased organs.

This sort of intense research is helpful not only for acupuncture
but for all energy medicine, which we look at more in chapter 15.

All medical investigations can only tell the doctor what is going on *now*, after organic breakdown has occurred. But when information is accessed from the energy systems of the body, problems can be detected much earlier, when they are probably easier to deal with.

Healing research

During 1987 the study *Factors determining the success of nicotine withdrawal* involved 532 smokers and demonstrated that religious commitment and prayer for healing produced much long-term success. Since then, reported *Readers' Digest* in 2002, other studies have shown how committed people tend to live longer, have better recoveries from illnesses, tougher hearts, lower blood pressure, really good mental health, and reduced stress.

More scientific research has now been conducted into healing than any other therapy, in some cases involving prayer, and often touch. We saw in connection with Question 8 how wounded mice healed faster through touch. Using gamma ray photography various experiments have demonstrated how during laying-on-of-hands the beta brainwaves of the channels and the receivers both changed to alpha ones, indicating at least that something is happening that is more potent than casual touch. And it is clear from much research that when healing is effective there is an interchange of energy between healer and person healed.

American psychiatrist Dr Daniel Benor, who lives in England, is a leading expert in this field. He has led well over a hundred experiments into healing. About two-thirds of his controlled trials have demonstrated the positive effects of healing. Though many of the studies are flawed in minor aspects, and some of them in major ways, there remain a convincing number of excellent studies with significant results.

The objections of others

Medical objections

Some doctors only accept treatments tested in the same manner as drugs. It is suggested by some practitioners that such doctors are doubly blinded by the double blind placebo trials: once because they refuse to accept any form of healing treatment unless it has been evidenced by these trials, and doubly because natural therapies have so much to offer to complement the good work that the doctors themselves are doing. It is arrogant to suggest that a therapy is automatically flawed if it does not neatly fit into our normal way of proving things. In any case, absence of proof does not indicate proof of absence.

According to *What Doctors Don't Tell You* at the turn of this century, when addressing the National Institute for Clinical Excellence, the Chairman of the British Medical Association Ethics Committee stated that at least half of the present medical treatments are useless. If this is so, and yet these treatments continue to be used, should we reject complementary medicine for the same reason? There are good quality trials being undertaken in connection with therapies, but they do not find their way into prestigious medical journals, so doctors may have to become detectives to find them! Other trials could well be undertaken if only the facilities, time and money were available, as they are to pharmaceutical companies. Meanwhile, we could embrace the overwhelming general evidence that therapies usually work, and weigh each situation on its own merits.

Christian objections

Some Christians believe that what current science cannot explain must be supernatural and that, when this is applied to therapies practised by non-Christians, they must have a demonic source. But many concepts like this have been believed by Christians down the centuries and later scientifically demonstrated to be incorrect. They have frequently been the consequence of superstitious fears.

The proof of prayer

During an Oprah Winfrey show televised in this country, Dr Larry Dossey reported on an amazing study that took place at San Francisco Hospital during the 1990s involving 400 heart patients. Two hundred were chosen at random to be prayed for and the others were not. Neither the patients nor their doctors were told which were which. After a year more people died in the group not prayed for. The people who did not receive prayer were five times more likely to require antibiotics and three times more probable to develop complications. All twelve people who required ventilators were also in this group. As well as this study, a battery of two hundred controlled tests was also conducted. Prayer was shown to produce a positive effect on everything from cancer and heart disease in humans to laboratory tests made on white blood cells.

One study by Dan Benor was of born-again Christians who prayed for healing for 192 patients. Those praying were given the patients' first names, their diagnoses, and updates on their condition. Each intercessor prayed daily for a rapid recovery and for prevention of complications and death, plus further things thought beneficial. Another 201 patients served as a control group. Between the groups there were no significant differences in any variables that might have influenced the results, so the study was rigorously accurate. The 109 patients in both groups with acute heart attacks were specifically compared and no significant differences were found.

Significantly fewer patients prayed for required any ventilation or antibiotics, had cardiopulmonary arrests, developed pneumonia, had congestive heart failure or required diuretics. Despite these differences between the two groups the duration of their stay in the cardiac intensive care unit and in hospital remained similar.

If healing were a drug ...

Dr Benor concludes that action at a distance, and yet without intervening mechanical or conventional energy mechanisms, forces the medics and scientists to consider unconventional explanations. He has successfully shown that healing therapy is more than placebo – unless enzymes, yeasts, bacteria, plants and mice are subject to suggestion! He believes that, if healing were a drug, it would be accepted as effective on the basis of the evidence he has produced.

While there is still much research to do, Christians can safely make use of many therapies, as long as these are pleasing to God and we are guided by Him and His written word the Bible. But what does that mean? We shall explore this more in the next chapter.

Practical discussion questions

1. When is scientific evidence absolutely necessary in orthodox medicine, osteopathic treatment and Christian healing ministry?

2. A Christian tells you, 'I would never enter a health food store because of the New Age products there.' What is your response?

3. Why should someone pay to see an acupuncturist when he or she could get painkillers from a doctor for the cost of a prescription?

4. 'More things are wrought by prayer than this world dreams of.' How far can prayer for healing be measured? (Ephesians 3:20)

Question 12: Scriptural Backing

Should We Accept Therapies Which Have No Biblical Authority?

The answer to this question is a qualified yes. Some therapies are specifically mentioned and encouraged in Scripture; others are not mentioned there but are in line with Christian teaching; others are acceptable to Christians within certain limitations, while yet others contrast directly with what the Bible teaches. Here I am expressing the definite views held by Breath Ministries and emphasising our positive approach to complementary therapies.

We accept all types of therapy mentioned in Scripture

There are at least twelve activities in the Bible which could be classed as therapies, and these are all used in some form today.

Three which include direct contact

1. Christian healing
This is the only therapy which was specifically authorised and commanded by Jesus. When He sent out His twelve apostles, '[they] *anointed many sick people with oil and healed them'* (Mark 6:13). Later He also commanded the seventy-two 'lay people' to heal the sick (Luke 10:9). And when He sent out the eleven apostles before His ascension to preach the gospel He promised,

> '... *these signs will accompany those who believe ... they will place their hands on sick people, and they will get well.'*
> (Mark 16:17–18)

Therefore, as we have already seen in previous chapters, every Christian has been commissioned to share the healing love of Jesus in some way. This ministry is for all areas: relationship with God, physical healing, inner healing (of mind, will and emotions), deliverance from evil, restoring of relationships and healing of circumstances. Jesus has promised to do whatever we ask in His name (John 14:14).

2. Touch

> *'He* [Jesus] *touched her hand and the fever left her.'*
> (Matthew 8:15)

As we observed in discussing Question 8, touch can be powerful, therapeutic, and a means of healing. The Lord used it frequently and naturally, as did His followers: not just the apostles but other Christians too, such as Ananias (Acts 9:17). It is a major method of healing in the Church today, expressed especially through the laying-on-of-hands (e.g. Acts 28:8), but through anointing with oil as well (e.g. James 5:14). Touch is also an important factor in therapies such as osteopathy, chiropractic, reflexology and aromatherapy.

3. The spoken word

Jesus frequently brought about healing through the spoken word. Often it was with a command prayer, such as in Matthew 8:3: *'Be clean!'* On other occasions the healing followed a 'message of knowledge' (1 Corinthians 12:8), such as to the centurion:

> *'Go! It will be done just as you believed it would.'*
> (Matthew 8:13)

Christians need to pray for the right words to use in healing ministry. The spoken word is also a major tool of counselling and psychotherapy.

Three which influence dietary requirements

1. Nutritional therapy

Nutritional therapy is guided use of food to improve our health, for what we choose to eat every day of our lives will inevitably affect our health. We are what we eat: *'As a man eats, so is he'!* (cf. Proverbs 23:7, AV). The Book of Leviticus contains rules of hygiene and laws to help distinguish which foods were most health-giving, while in Daniel we grasp how beneficial a well-balanced diet is (Daniel 1:15). The nutritional therapist today similarly seeks to advise and to encourage the use of nutrients, vitamins and balanced diet that can aid health and fitness and consequently can lead to healing.

2. Herbal medicine

Doctor Luke (Colossians 4:14), who appears to be enthusiastic about both medical skills and spiritual healing gifts, was almost certainly an herbalist. Herbs played a large part in alleviating physical suffering during Bible times. Today plants are still used to make medicines, as they have been for thousands of years, and these are provided in the form of teas, tinctures and tablets. They are also used as supportive treatment in even serious conditions. Herbs are perfectly safe in the right hands, but Christians will want to ensure that herbalists are properly trained and qualified.

3. Fasting

Jesus' words **'When** *you fast'* (not *'If'* – Matthew 6:16) remind us that He took it for granted that His followers would fast, as did the Jews. In addition to the desirability of fasting as an aid to prayer and guidance, it has proved invaluable in connection with health and fitness, to the extent that some have testified, 'Fasting can save your life' (see Question 31). When Jesus' disciples failed to deliver the epileptic boy He gave as one reason, *'This kind can come forth by nothing, but by prayer and fasting'* (Mark 9:29, AV).

Three which incorporate deep relaxation

1. Rest

In the context of rest, Psalm 23:2 uses a strong Hebrew word, *'He* **makes** *me lie down in green pastures.'* And Jesus' words in Matthew 11:28 can be translated, *'Come to me, all you who are weary and burdened, and I will* **make** *you rest.'* Learning how to rest and sleep, today sometimes by using relaxation techniques, aids health and fitness. Sometimes people may have an ability to relax ministered to them. They may then need other aids to help them make use of this ability. Some healing homes and retreat centres provide relaxation tapes.

2. Dreams

> *'You discern my going out and my lying down.'*   (Psalm 139:3)

It is helpful to commit our sleeping lives into the hands of the Lord. Although many of our dreams reflect our activities of the past day or our concerns about the future, God can also speak to people through dreams, as He did to both Joseph in the Old

Testament (Genesis 37:5) and Joseph in the New (Matthew 2:13). We sleep today for approximately one-third of our lives, but we shall only be refreshed and strengthened sufficiently if our dreams do not drastically disturb our sleep, so dream therapy may be required.

3. Meditation

The psalmist loved to meditate on both the words and works of God (Psalm 119:15 and 27). And meditation is another therapy which has been shown scientifically and medically to benefit people in body and mind. However, as we saw in connection with Question 9, we can recommend scriptural and contemplative meditation but not transcendental.

Three which involve diligent attention

1. Aromatherapy

From Queen Esther (Esther 2:12) to the extravagant gesture of Mary, the sister of Lazarus, in anointing Jesus' feet and His hair (John 12:3) the use of oils runs through the Bible. And today aromatherapy is a popular therapeutic treatment which enhances well-being, relieves stress, and promotes vitality and good health. Some essential oils have a stimulating effect upon the body, mind and emotions, while others have a calming influence. Often inhaled or applied by massage, oils can also be added to a warm bath, or used to make fragrant a relaxing room, along with flowers, candles and soft music. In addition they can be used in the home as basic first aid, such as the treatment of common colds and minor cuts.

2. Music

When King Saul was oppressed by an evil spirit, he was soothed by David playing the harp for him (1 Samuel 16:23). Similarly, when I suffered from depression in 1977 I could not bear loud music but the soothing tones of a record by blind pianist Marilyn Baker were just what I needed. Music and dance therapy lift the spirit, especially if enhanced by true worship, skill, beauty or laughter.

3. Exercise

> '... *physical training is of some value* ... '   (1 Timothy 4:8)

Paul was familiar with the Olympic Games and the notion that regular sport or exercise not only keeps the body fit but the whole person too. Today particular exercises may be recommended by physiotherapists and practitioners, while other people are able to build up their stamina by walking, swimming, climbing, or working out in the gym.

We accept many therapies that are not contrary to Bible teaching

Some Christians adopt the attitude of 'condemnation without investigation' towards alternative therapies, but remember Proverbs 14:15 (Amplified Version):

> *'The simpleton believes every word he hears, but the prudent man looks and considers well where he is going.'*

We should not be swayed by hearsay comment or general assumptions.

There are a number of things which Christians of the twenty-first century accept that are not mentioned in Scripture. Some obvious examples are aeroplanes, computers and television. So the right question to ask about an alternative therapy is not, 'Is it in the Bible?' but 'Is it consistent with scriptural teaching or contrary to it?'

Let me list twelve popular therapies which are practised and used by Christian people as well as others today. I believe God uses them all to bring healing *where they are in the right hands*, for in their pure forms they are in line with Christian teaching.

Three 'manipulation' therapies

1. Osteopathy
Concentrating on adjustment of bones and muscles, the therapist treats the problem area (e.g. back pain) but also looks for root causes and, using manipulative and soft-tissue skills, treats the whole person and gives advice to prevent more structural problems. Chris sees most patients at least three times. The first session involves taking a case history, an examination and treatment of the immediate problem. Later she treats the other areas affected.

2. Chiropractic

Chiropractic is similar to osteopathy, viewing the spine as the key part of body structure and stressing its role in protecting the nervous system. But it mainly uses manipulation. Scientific research has found it to be effective for acute lower back pain.

3. Alexander Technique

This aims to improve mental and physical well-being by correcting posture. The technique, normally taught on a one-to-one basis, teaches you how to use your body with a minimum amount of strain and injury, plus how to assess your posture and how to correct it.

Three 'estimation' therapies

1. Homoeopathy

This is strictly speaking an alternative more than a complementary therapy, as its remedies may be used in place of orthodox medicine. It is founded on the principle that 'like cures like', so that a substance producing symptoms of an illness in a healthy person will cure a sick person developing the same symptoms. From a very thorough case-history the practitioner estimates and prescribes the remedy which will match precisely the patient's condition. Some chemists sell homoeopathic remedies for domestic use as well.

2. Acupuncture

Acupuncture forms a major part of Traditional Chinese Medicine. The acupuncturist inserts fine needles at specific points on the person's body to clear blockages in the meridians (channels of energy) and initiate healing. Nowadays sterile disposable needles are used, and the acupuncture points will often be warmed by using smouldering herbs. Acupressure and shiatsu massage therapies work on the same basis, using pressure instead of needles to stimulate the sensitive points, namely those of least electrical resistance.

3. Kinesiology

This is founded on the principle that certain muscle groups are related to specific parts of the body. The muscles are tested to detect and correct imbalances in energy flow. Practitioners often include some massage, dietary advice, and counselling, if required.

Three 'application' therapies

1. Reflexology
Reflexology involves applying pressure to certain points on the feet which are known as reflex areas. The qualified practitioner is able to massage or manipulate these points and to bring about immediate release of energy. The points relate to specific regions and organs of the body, which is divided into zones and channels of energy. The aim is again to remove blockages and speed healing.

2. Massage
Massage combines the healing power of touch with other techniques to become a therapy. Some types of massage work on pressure points and others on specific conditions. For example, remedial massage is used for sports injuries or muscle strain. Manual Lymphatic Drainage (MLD) stimulates the lymph system to eliminate toxins. Some massage practitioners are known as manipulative therapists.

3. Naturopathy
Naturopaths allow the body to respond using natural substances rather than drugs, discouraging 'toxic overload'. Natural means used to maintain health and fitness include air, water, sunlight, magnetism and electricity, some exercise and relaxation, a diet of fresh foods, and sometimes 'the prayer of faith' (James 5:15)!

Three 'explanation' therapies

1. Bach Flower Remedies
Pronounced 'Batch' these are homoeopathically prepared plant- and flower-based remedies, each specially devised to treat a different feeling. Olive, for example, is considered excellent for exhaustion. Beneficial in themselves, they should, however, be avoided when some therapists put astrological signs over them and interpret them accordingly.

2. Psychotherapy
This form of psychological help for emotional difficulties makes use of the relationship between patient and therapist, through talking, of the patient's thoughts and feelings. Confidential help

is given to people with all kinds of problems as they bring out past memories and present concerns that affect their situations. Psychotherapists can help clients to understand themselves better and to make more satisfying or lasting relationships with others.

3. Counselling

Forms of counselling exist for most problems! Counsellors help people by listening, asking questions, and sometimes making suggestions. In prayer counselling Christians listen at length and minister in depth using the laying-on-of-hands, not generally giving advice but allowing the Lord to speak through gifts of the Spirit. Life coaching is quite different, as it ignores the past and helps individuals to get from where they are to where they want to be.

We regard some therapies as only acceptable within limitations

Let me give three examples of these 'borderline' activities. I would only use these when in the hands of committed Christians.

1. Crystal therapy

Crystals, which can vibrate at similar levels to the body's own energy, are placed around you or on the parts of your body which need healing. In themselves these crystals are good, part of God's creation. But the problem is that so many crystal therapists are into New Age activities which they import into their treatment. The same sort of concerns apply to magnet or polarity therapy.

2. Hypnotherapy

Hailed as successful in such areas as helping people to give up smoking, this is thought to work by tapping into the unconscious. Therapists put clients in a trance-like state where they feel more relaxed and can concentrate on changing thoughts, behaviour or feelings. The problem is that their mind becomes more under the control of another person than in most other forms of medicine. If a Christian decides to make use of this therapy, we advise him or her to claim the protection of the blood of Jesus, to bind the enemy from the treatment, and to commit the situation into the hands of God.

3. Yoga

Much of Yoga philosophy is not compatible with Christian beliefs. When we took our monthly Praise, Healing and Renewal services in Horsham Town Hall, West Sussex, we felt it right to cleanse the building before each meeting, as some people could sense a harmful atmosphere following a regular yoga class there. Some Christians, however, are quite happy to do just the exercises (hatha yoga), and as they do so they sing to the Holy Spirit songs like 'Breathe on me, Breath of God' or 'Spirit of the living God, fall afresh on me'.

We reject 'therapies' which go against what the Bible teaches

Again I give three examples. Ones like these are dealt with more fully in connection with Questions 26 and 29 on harmful experiences and spiritism.

1. Past-life regression

In the next chapter we shall see how reincarnation is contrary to orthodox Christian beliefs. Therefore – while we minister for healing of the family tree and setting people free from harmful influences in their ancestral line (Exodus 20:4) – we can see no value whatever in dragging up experiences in so-called past lives.

2. Spiritualist healing

Spiritualists tend to call this 'Psychic healing', but this is not simply mind over matter. It involves 'consulting spirits of the dead for guidance', mediums and séances, all of which Scripture tells us that God detests (Deuteronomy 18:10–12).

3. Tarot reading

Tarot card reading is one of many forms of fortune-telling, all of which are substitutes for faith and guidance. To rely on it to prevent illness is both fraudulent and dangerous (Matthew 7:15). There are manifestly more helpful routes to healing and wholeness available to us in the realms of medicine, ministry and therapy.

Practical discussion questions

1. How is your church obeying Jesus' command to heal the sick (Luke 10:9)? Does it take account of complementary medicine?

2. How important are dieting and fasting for health and fitness? How can nutritional therapy and naturopathy help with this?

3. Do you or any of your friends have difficulty relaxing? Which therapies have proved most useful in helping you to relax?

4. How do you regard the last three 'therapies' in this chapter? Are there other therapies you would be unhappy about using? Why?

Question 13: Taking Control
How Can I Be Responsible for My Health If the Lord Is in Control?

Three major factors will often distinguish complementary medicine from orthodox procedures, all relating to the person's lifestyle:

1. distrust of drugs alone, in favour of using non-toxic remedies
2. desire to find root causes, as people are treated holistically
3. direct involvement: the individual takes control of his or her health.

It is the last of these which troubles some Christians, as they see a conflict with their taking charge when they have invited the Lord to take complete control of every part of their lives (Romans 12:1). This even prevents some from consulting a complementary therapist.

The need to respond to God's work

Robots or responsible?
There need be no cause for concern here. God does not want people to be like robots, and He has given us free will. So as a Christian I have placed myself under *His* control but He is depending on me to *take* control of things for which I am responsible, one of which is my health (Matthew 6:25). He wants me to be guided by Him but not to be manipulated by Him like a puppet on a string. We have seen in connection with Question 2 how it is important for us to co-operate with Him in whatever

ways He chooses to heal us, so we will want to ensure that we know and do His will (Psalm 27:11). But part of that will is that we each play our part by using the good means He has provided.

So we do not need to strive at taking control, or to be afraid of losing control: yet we are responsible for our own actions. This is one reason why Christians should have nothing to do with the beliefs made popular by the New Age movement about reincarnation.

Reincarnation

A man once came up to me for healing ministry and stated casually, 'I have a lot of baggage from previous births.' I knew instantly that he had embraced the idea of reincarnation, of someone returning to life in another form. This is closely allied to the philosophy of karma, in which every person is regarded as master of his or her own destiny. It involves justification by works rather than by faith (contrast Galatians 2:16). Material is regarded as basically evil, so adherents are encouraged to 'shake off the material by getting involved in the spiritual'. Then they are thought to be released through many incarnations, some 800 before being fully purified. So good or bad conduct determines what one becomes in each birth.

Whatever the reasons for people thinking they have existed before (hypnotherapists say past lives are fantasised), the idea is false. There are at least fifteen Scripture references that go against the idea. One of the clearest is Hebrews 9:27: *'man is destined to die once, and after that to face judgement.'* And this is where reincarnation is contrary to the need for each one of us to take control under God and be responsible for our own actions. For if we each come back in another form, which of our incarnations will be responsible on Judgement Day? If Adolf Hitler returned as Mother Teresa, which of them would be judged? So reincarnation takes away our personal responsibility. In any case it's unnecessary. We can look forward to something better than reincarnation: resurrection!

The need to receive our healing

For many people the only way of receiving their healing is simply by taking the tablets the doctor gives them. But if we are to take control of our health under God, we are often able to do much more.

Ill people unable to get to our meetings have sometimes purchased our cassettes, and after listening to one they have put a hand on the tape and found blessing. A lady at Eastbourne who had shingles placed one of our cassettes against her body and trusted the Lord to heal her, and He did (cf. Acts 19:11–12). Obviously her faith was in Jesus, not an inanimate object, but the act of touching it in the context of faith brought about the change that was needed.

Once I was asked, 'Won't it be selfish for me to come forward for ministry when others are far worse off?' I replied, 'No. If there are others present who are obviously very ill or in terrible pain, it's good that you should let them come first. But you are entitled to receive your healing – not because of anything you've done but because it's part of the inheritance the Lord Jesus has won for you on the cross.'

It is harder for people who are constantly taking responsibility for others' needs, such as doctors and clergy, to ask for help for themselves. A lady social worker at one of our training days left it right until the end of the day before asking for ministry. But she was glad that she did. She had a fear of being a passenger in a car, since her father had died as one. But her fears evaporated.

Another way to receive healing is in James 5:16 (Amplified Version):

> *'Confess to one another . . . your faults . . . that you may be healed.'*

In the group context this is best when it arises naturally during sharing or prayer, especially before receiving communion. It can be a liberating experience if sensitively guided by able leaders.

Mentally ill and handicapped people may be unable to take the same kind of responsibility for their health as others, so in this case we encourage them to receive help as best they can. We pray that they will get to the point where they can respond more positively.

The need to resource our bodies

Balance in our bodies
Jesus asked, *'Is not . . . the body more important than clothes?'* (Matthew 6:25), and Paul asked, *'Do you not know that your body is a temple of the Holy Spirit . . . ?'* (1 Corinthians 6:19). Our bodies are precious to God. In fact, a temple is a place of worship and

sacrifice, so we have a particular responsibility to ensure that God is worshipped and sacrificed to in our bodies. This includes taking care of them and using every means He provides to keep them healthy and balanced.

Jesus lived a wholly balanced life. He made plans for the future that were in line with His Father's will, for example He set His face like a flint to go to Jerusalem (Luke 9:51). But He lived one day at a time, not getting anxious about the next (Matthew 6:34). Sometimes, when we do not live like that, God may cause us to stop. He may allow us to lie upon beds of sickness so that we have time to reassess our priorities. And often the balance is not restored until we learn to do less in certain areas (cf. Luke 10:40–42).

Loss of voluntary control?

We saw in the last chapter how many therapies can help us to keep our bodies balanced. But each therapy is simply an aid. It is up to us to take control so that we ensure the balance is maintained. Strangely, it is this very point that is the focus of one criticism of kinesiology. Some ask, 'What force suddenly renders a limb weak or even powerless the very instant some foods or other substance touch the client's lips or skin?' In fact, feelings of weakness and powerlessness are not uncommon in the healing ministry, as we shall explore more in answer to Question 33. This results from a release of energy that can be something God wants and the person submits to.

But no actual loss of voluntary control truly occurs in correctly applied kinesiology, and the client's 'loss of strength' is only apparent because of using a muscle isolated to test energy flow. So the 'force' used in kinesiology, as in the other complementary therapies, is natural energy that comes from a supernatural God.

Abundant life

Sometimes we have a choice about how to take control. This could give an opportunity for the Christian to seek the Lord about the best route to take – though He has also given us our common sense!

A woman with chronic asthma discovered this could be relieved by using steroid inhalants prescribed by her GP. But she wished to take control of the situation herself, so she went to a therapist and used visualisation techniques, which proved just as effective.

A lady vicar wrote to us saying that she benefited from visiting a Christian beauty therapist who gave her an aromatherapy massage. The vicar found that her general health had improved through this and especially through the management of stress. Under God she had taken responsibility for her health. She added this in her letter:

> 'I am inclined to believe that in ignoring complementary medicine and therapies we are missing something consistent with Christ's promise of abundant life (John 10:10).'

I am sure she is right, and I think we are only just beginning to see how abundant it is!

Practical discussion questions

1. In which other ways can we take care of our bodies? (Matthew 6:25)

2. How can we best confess our faults to one another? (James 5:16)

3. How should we minister to the mentally ill, mentally retarded, mentally disabled and mentally handicapped? (Luke 4:18–19)

4. How can Christian leaders encourage a response? (Acts 3:6–8)

Question 14: Natural Remedies
Is It Safe and Helpful to Make Use of Natural Remedies?

Christine and I were once walking on Tunbridge Wells common, only a short distance from the Breath Centre and from where we live. It was a lovely summer's evening and, as we held hands and walked under the trees, we were drinking in the beauty of God's creation. Then my wife exclaimed, 'Doesn't it minister to you!' and her words seemed entirely appropriate, for the Lord can also minister to us through nature and natural means. I use the word 'natural' here in the sense of 'free to everyone'. And though there are some plants and natural substances that are poisonous, and some have had old wives' tales attached to them, most are safer than drugs, and many are helpful in aiding the healing process when supervised by competent people.

It's only natural

Some Christians are worried about using natural means because the Authorised Version of the Bible describes the person without the Holy Spirit as 'the natural man' (1 Corinthians 2:14). They conclude that natural means are associated with unforgiven sin. But, though people are by nature sinful, that does not mean all natural things are bad, for *'everything God created is good, and nothing is to be rejected'* (1 Timothy 4:4), and *'God ... richly provides us with everything for our enjoyment'* (1 Timothy 6:17) – so natural remedies are good.

Since so much sickness is caused by violating the natural laws that God made, in one sense sickness is not natural! So it is logical that some of its most effective antidotes should be found in the realm of natural remedies. The medical herbalist, for instance, treats clients by restoring a balance in their body through use of natural substances that are opposites to what they are suffering.

Natural environments

The right environment

One of the ways we can help counteract the pollution of our world environment is through using the natural means God has provided. But the environment in which a sick person seeks to get well is also important – whether at home, church, hospital or clinic. A therapist expressed it cogently when he said, 'I provide the right environment and allow the body to heal.'

Psalm 23 is full of different environments in which we can trust the Good Shepherd to lead, restore, guide, protect, feed and house His sheep: green pastures (v. 2), quiet waters (v. 2), paths of righteousness (v. 3), the valley of the shadow of death (v. 4), the presence of one's enemies (v. 5), the house of the Lord (v. 6). We can see how these different environments are a combination of natural and spiritual ones and they are all conducive to healing.

The wrong environment

Sometimes, having been completely healed, people may have to return to a troubled environment that may have contributed to their condition. Until either that environment is changed, or they are able to leave it, their problems may reappear, so they will need further help.

The human body can contend with a tremendous amount of

abuse but there is a limit, and that may be manifested in physical problems. Have you ever wondered why Christians (including 'spiritual' ones) get sick as much as other people? It could be partly because they are not making use of natural therapists. It may also be because many physical problems are caused by poor eating habits, lifestyle and lack of exercise. The sick person can expect to be helped by natural remedies supplied by therapists but also by deliberately making use themselves of natural means. Let's look at some of these.

Natural nutrients

Processed foods

The nutritional therapist and naturopath prescribe specific diets for each client they see. They may also test for food intolerances. Nutrients are all but totally destroyed in processing foods now, and with additives, colourings and fats, etc., the result is less healthy nourishment. We do not all need to be health food freaks or vegetarians to eat healthily, but, even with laws requiring the manufacturers to specify details of ingredients, it can still be difficult to ascertain from labels on packets and tins just what ingredients and how much goodness they contain. A leading naturopath reckoned that sometimes the cardboard in which some items are wrapped is of more nutritional value than the food itself! Yet organic and healthier foods can be more expensive.

Radical reform

But people are becoming more aware of the need to eat healthily, and there is a gradual increase in those who do. Before 1940 most of our food was organic. There were no pesticides and fungicides to damage it. But we are now so used to devouring fast foods and processed items that we are unlikely to jettison these. However, we have learned from natural therapists the value of eating fresh or frozen fruits and vegetables when we can. Many people have also become conscious that if we do not drink enough water we can quickly experience tiredness, fatigue or exhaustion. And we are aware of so many people with allergies, which frequently means that the liver is not able to tolerate certain foods. All this and much more points to the need for radical reform in our eating habits. Nutritionists and naturopaths can help with this, not only when we are sick but when we wish to prevent sickness happening.

Vitamin supplements

Vitamin supplements are more than one hundred per cent safer than prescribed medicines and many over-the-counter drugs. But attempts have been made to classify vitamins and herbs in similar ways to orthodox drugs. This is as difficult as endeavouring to test all complementary medicines by the double blind placebo test that we have already looked at. There is definitely need for regulation of these and other natural substances, as well as for much more information, but on a different basis. During illness people are likely to need more vitamins than when they are well, so this is an important area. Christians are praying for the best solution.

Natural resources

Quality of life

When the human body is healthy it works well. Energy gets to the different parts of it in the right amount. But to maintain this we need to keep body, soul and spirit in balance (1 Thessalonians 5:23). Christians see this as including our relationship and fellowship with God, while others who speak of 'spirituality' may not include this. But there is a common agreement among complementary therapists that quality of life is important, and that progress can often best be made by individuals changing their attitudes and lifestyle.

All things natural

It is this that naturopaths particularly emphasise, as they treat people with 'all things natural'. It was the naturopaths who first called for hospital windows to be opened, and for sickly people to get away to the seaside or the mountains, all with the simple purpose of taking in fresher, cleaner air. Today there are so many people with asthma and respiratory problems on account of carbon dioxide emissions from vehicles on city roads and other polluted sources. Such people can often derive great benefit from natural resources.

Naturopaths help cleanse the client's body of all that is keeping it from being healthy, and strengthen it with natural resources. Since they believe every acute disease is the response of the body to something it wishes to eliminate (cf. Mark 7:20), this cleansing enables the body to function better. They never expect a cure for the common cold because the cold *is* the cure! Sir William Lane, world authority on medical topics and top British abdominal surgeon, said, 'We've been studying germs when we should have been studying diet and drainage. Drain the body of its poisons, feed it properly, and the miracle is done!'

Other resources
Burrswood has a hydrotherapy pool where I once baptised a teenage girl. Hydrotherapy is another natural resource, as, for example, are cold or hot compresses, which are used to divert the circulation. Of the many ways in which we can be helped to relax, humour is something that Jesus Himself used. He pictured a camel squeezing through the eye of the needle (Matthew 19:24), a man trying to remove a speck from his brother's eye when he had a plank in his own (Matthew 7:3–5), and the Pharisees straining a gnat and swallowing a camel (Matthew 23:24).

Balanced lives
Involvement in sport or other exercise is one of the most helpful ways of letting out our anger and aggression, rather than taking it out on our loved ones or bottling it up. The Lord will not mind if we also shout at Him sometimes, as the psalmist may have done when he could not understand what God was doing (e.g. Psalm 42:9). And it's so necessary that we have days off and leisure time. We can become ill if we overdo things, do not get enough sleep or do not take holidays. It is difficult to live balanced lives every day, but the Lord wants to help us to maintain a balance over a period. A certain man who was one of the 20 per cent of people who suffer from 80 per cent of the diseases, constantly asked his doctor for pills. In the surgery one day he said, 'Doctor, give me medication!' The doctor ordered, 'Give me your diary.' The man did, and the doctor tore out three months' pages. '*There's* your medication!' he cried.

Practical discussion questions
1. Name ways in which creation has ministered to you (Psalm 19:1).
2. Do you know sick people in poor environments? How can you help?
3. What foods are you swallowing – physical, mental and spiritual?
4. What fresh resources could help you lead a more balanced life?

Question 15: **Releasing Energy**
Why Are Some Christians So Fearful of Energy?

Some who quite enthusiastically emphasise the Holy Spirit's power and who minister Christian healing are very suspicious of energy. In fact, I've known some Christians who are terrified if it is mentioned! Though they may believe that people have sometimes become ill by living in proximity to power cables, they refuse to accept that any energy medicine can have the opposite effect and is something that God has provided. In some cases they exhibit a superstitious fear of becoming demonised as a result. There are three primary reasons for such concern, and the first is by far the commonest.

New Age associations

The New Age movement has hijacked complementary therapies, which use energy medicine, by involving many therapists in practices with which Christians disagree. Christians rightly only wish to consult practitioners who are not involved in questionable activities or at least whose treatment is not adversely affected by these.

One part of New Age philosophy with which Christians disagree is that *everything* should be seen in terms of energy. This leaves no room for original sin or the Holy Spirit, and the New Age idea of 'awakening the spirit within' is a very different one from the experience of releasing the Holy Spirit's power (John 7:37–39). Strict New Agers do not think of 'spirit' as either our human spirit (as in *'spirit, soul and body'*: 1 Thessalonians 5:23) or the Holy Spirit, but as the person's inner self or inner energy.

God's gift of healing energy
Yet, like many of these therapies, energy is good in itself. It is something that God created – one of His good gifts (James 1:17). Even if it is called the vital force or life-force, or described in Eastern terms, the energy released in complementary medicine is neither magic nor satanic, but a gift of God which can be used in healing. And we have already seen that it features in a range of therapies.

In *A Christian's Guide to Homoeopathy*, Alan Crook states:

> 'Biophysics has now shown that every living being possesses an electromagnetic energy field. This controls all the organism's vital functions, and, if its resonance is disturbed, the vital functions are disturbed. This energy is a natural phenomenon. It is neither the invention nor the property of any one culture, religion or philosophy. Because western orthodox medicine deals only with physical, material aspects of the human organism, it has chosen to overlook this, but every other major system of medicine in the world takes it into account. There is nothing occult or demonic about it, and there is no reason to fear it.' (p. 78)

When this author writes about the energy field 'controlling' an organism, it is in the sense that it stimulates it or parts of it to act and react in particular ways. This corresponds to what scientists mean when they speak of the brain, the heart, or the nervous system 'controlling' the functions of a living being. It in no way detracts from the control that God has over our lives.

How energy aids healing

For three hundred years the West has been using healing remedies related mainly to chemistry (drugs). In future we are likely to see more related to physics (using energy). We have already noted in response to Question 11 how much scientific research has demonstrated that, when energy medicine is effective, there is always an interchange of energy between the person in need and the channel of healing.

In the 'vital force therapies', such as homoeopathy, acupuncture, reflexology, kinesiology and healing, one of the main aims is to stimulate the energies of the body to heal itself. The release of energy may be triggered off by different stimuli: the touch, the needles, the homoeopathic remedy, the prayer, the anointing, etc.; but the results can be the same, as in each case this energy is directed to where it is most needed in order to accelerate the healing that God desires for us. What Christians need to beware of is not in most cases the actual therapies used to trigger this release of energy, but the other philosophies and dubious practices which sometimes can play such a large part in the life and work of the alternative practitioner that they influence the treatment given and can sometimes cause Satan to get a hold on the client: these include astrology, fortune-telling, pendulum swinging, spiritism, etc., and those New Age beliefs which are clearly contrary to Scripture.

New Age philosophies

The New Age movement is a broad term enveloping a vast assortment of differing groups and philosophies. It incorporates everything from holistic health groups to pyramid power groups. We should not condemn everything in the movement but build on those interests that are common to both New Agers and Christians. One of these is an often healthy attitude to the world's environment. Imminent destruction of the rain forests, the extinction of threatened species of birds and animals, and the evidence that some farming methods are an offence against nature, are all common concerns.

On the other hand, the New Age movement contains many elements of Hinduism, Buddhism and Confucianism, and it asserts that all world religions have common truths (contrast Colossians 2:8). A key uniting element among the different groups of the movement is a belief in self-improvement through practices like meditation. Contacting spiritual forces is often thought to be achieved by acquiring strange powers and chasing after mystical experiences.

One popular philosophy is monism – 'all is one' – and a consequent aim in healing is to balance all contrasting forces, the *yin* and the *yang*, which are thought to proceed from the *ch'i* (energy). Many Christian people can happily accept the value of a therapist removing obstructions in people's bodies and helping to restore balance – an important feature of most therapies – but not that the concepts of good and evil, for instance, have to be balanced.

Another popular philosophy among New Agers is pantheism, the idea that God is in everything regardless. While we see His presence in every part of His creation (Psalm 139:7–10), they view god as a force into which those who attain enlightenment can tap. 'Nature' and 'Mother Earth' can so easily become the equivalent of a transcendent God, as in paganism and white witchcraft, and the creation becomes in practice equivalent to the creator (contrast Isaiah 40:25–26). In practice God the Father does not exist outside creation, Jesus is not unique (just another guru), the Holy Spirit is only a force.

New Age monopoly?

Yet the fact that some people go to work by train does not mean that it is the only means of transport. And the fact that many New Agers use reflexology does not make that therapy New Age, any more than if orthodox medicine is used by Eskimos it becomes an Eskimo therapy. Why should New Agers monopolise complementary medicine? Why fear energy? As Alan Crook also asks: 'Are we to believe that God created electromagnetic energy solely for use by the devil?'

'Unscientific explanations'

A second reason why some Christians fear energy is that so many 'quacks' are associated with the field of energy medicine, the majority of therapies have not yet been regulated to ensure high standards, and they have not all provided sufficient demonstrable scientific evidence to satisfy most in the medical world.

Research

In my answer to Question 11 I referred to the research that has now been carried out, particularly in connection with acupuncture, nutrition, healing, touch and prayer. Yet I do not believe it is necessary for every treatment to be fully proven in the same way as some orthodox medical treatments are, especially in view of the fact that many of the latter have not been tested, nor have many of the healings claimed through Christian ministry. It is better to accept the overwhelming general evidence that these therapies normally work, and to weigh every situation on its own merits.

Regulation

This makes the matter of regulation even more important, however. Christians are rightly concerned that some therapists appear to have set themselves up with little training or qualifications. Under such circumstances it is necessary to ask questions about most practitioners before consulting them. Nevertheless, osteopathy and chiropractic have become a statutory part of primary health care in the UK, and other therapies are seeking to follow suit. As time progresses there is likely to be more regulation, so people will not be able to call themselves practitioners of a particular therapy unless registered nationally. This already applies to osteopaths and chiropractitioners. PACT provides a key to institutions which have trained and recognised safe and competent therapists (Appendix 3).

Supernatural manifestations

The other main reason why some Christians fear energy is because they tend to be frightened of anything considered supernatural: including speaking in tongues, exorcism, and falling under God's power. The fears they express may sometimes be because they are demonised themselves but in most cases it is simply that their particular backgrounds have not prepared them for any 'dramatic' manifestations of the Holy Spirit's power, and their fears can disappear as other Christians explain these manifestations lovingly to them.

Psychic experiences
While New Agers may teach how to produce and control alpha waves and to induce psychic experiences, Christians regard experiences such as resting in the Spirit (Revelation 1:17) as by-products, not to be engineered. Thus what is wrong for the Church is not the release of energy involved, nor is it the different level of consciousness to which people proceed, but *the way they arrive at that level.* God's way for us is not by means of hard drugs or transcendental meditation but by experiences like falling under the power of God or contemplative meditation on Jesus. Similarly Christians are not to dabble in astral projection, but it is quite different if, like Paul, we find ourselves having out-of-the-body experiences that we have not planned (2 Corinthians 12:1–10).

When a woman once touched the hem of His garment *'Jesus realised that power had gone out from him'* (Mark 5:30). Christians often feel energy flowing through as they lay on hands, and sometimes when they are simply within a healing atmosphere. But a number of non-Christians have experienced similar feelings. This may not be a sign of satanic power but of sensitivity to natural energy.

Spiritual power
However, the follower of Jesus is in a very privileged position. For when the therapist or minister of healing is a Spirit-filled Christian the Lord can provide a 'booster': He can add the Holy Spirit's *supernatural* power and gifts to aid the neutral process of releasing *natural* energy. Thus to natural and psychic gifts are added

charismatic gifts. But we require discernment to ensure that everything that happens is pleasing to Him (1 Corinthians 10:31). A lady at one of our training days told of how she seemed to be benefiting from the healing touch of a Brighton woman who spoke of God using her. But it then transpired that the 'healer' prayed to spirit guides each night, and further 'treatment' was refused.

Alongside provision of medicine, ministry and therapy we need the anointing of the Holy Spirit. When Christians have seen this in the form of lights above others – hence the haloes in the pictures of ancient saints – God has made visible the energy that is always there but normally *in*visible. Whether or not the anointing is seen or felt we aim to be transformed more and more into the likeness of Jesus Christ, the giver of life and health (2 Corinthians 3:18).

Practical discussion questions

1. How would you assist a fearful or concerned Christian to understand that energy is something God uses in healing?

2. Compare and contrast different means by which a release of energy can be triggered, in both medicine and ministry.

3. The minister of a church near where you live suggests that aromatherapy is 'unscientific'. What might your response be?

4. What examples of supernatural happenings are found in the Acts of the Apostles? What if one of these occurred today?

Guidance

Question 16: God's Clock
Isn't There a Right Time for Healing?

There are two possible meanings to this question and, as they are both quite important, I shall deal with them both in this chapter:

1. Isn't there a time known to God for a sick person to be cured?
2. Isn't there a right time for healing ministry to be on offer?

Now and then

The first meaning sometimes infers that those asking the question think that God doesn't want to heal them yet. If they have seen no improvement following prayer, they may be wondering if the Lord's plan is to heal them at a later date. They may also entertain the false idea that healing is a commodity to be obtained at some point in the future rather than (as we noticed in discussion of Question 1) a development of the work that God has begun in them.

God certainly knows, or can know if He desires to, when a person will be healed, and we have seen how one of the keys to healing is guidance, which means that among other things we will need to 'watch His clock' and follow His timing (Ecclesiastes 3:1). But that is very different from thinking that He may not wish to heal someone yet, for *'now is the day of salvation'* (wholeness – 2 Corinthians 6:2), and I believe the Lord desires to heal those who are sick as soon as possible.

Whatever will be will be?
As we explore this further, notice several other misunderstandings about God's guidance. One is the idea that 'whatever will be will be'. This fatalistic attitude is extremely common in Islam, where

the devout Muslim accepts that whatever happens, good or bad, 'It is the will of Allah'. How different is the way of Christ! Jesus taught that whatever *might* have been *need* not always be! And Christians believe that prayer *changes* things (e.g. James 5:15).

If we think that everything that happens to us is what God wants, then He wishes millions of people to remain unsaved and unhealed, to be sick and in pain! If instead we believe that He seldom gets His own way, and that sin and sickness are not a part of His plan, this is the God Jesus revealed (2 Peter 3:9). This raises tough questions, and I am conscious I have so much to learn, but Jesus asks us to trust Him when we don't understand what He is doing (John 13:7). We can be perfectly certain that He always wants the best for us.

If it is your will?

Some Christians also add 'If it is your will' to their prayers for healing. This is a helpful prayer to use when we are unsure about God's purposes but our consideration of Question 2 pointed up the truth that it *is* normally God's will to heal. If we say it when laying hands on the sick and needy,

1. we are then treating the Lord as if He cares less than we do;
2. we can unintentionally add a measure of doubt to our requests;
3. the sick person, on hearing our prayer, is hardly likely to be encouraged!

How much MORE!

A number of Christians also think that God wants to punish people with sickness. Christine and I have two grown-up sons, Stephen and Paul. When they were younger they misbehaved at times, but whenever I disciplined them I never said, 'This is the way I'll punish you: I'm going to make you sick!' And God is a much better father. Do those of us who are parents normally want our ill children to get better? Of course we do! And when do we want it to happen? Just as soon as possible! *How much more* does our heavenly Father normally want us whole, and as soon as possible! So the Lord allows sickness but He does not send it (cf. Job 2:6–7). And although we must die, unless Jesus first returns in body (1 Thessalonians 4:16), our loving Father would rather this be from old age than disease.

Life and death

In the case of Christians who are very old God may heal by taking them to be with Himself, but we once assumed God would do this when we laid hands on one old man and he was given several more years of life! In such instances it may then be necessary to know *how* God wishes to heal.

When people do die after we have prayed for them, it is often quickly and painlessly. But some Christians attempt to justify premature deaths by saying, 'It must have been the Lord's will to take him.' Though God would, indeed, have taken the Christian to be with Him, it was not God who took the person out of this world. God does not, for instance, plan that someone should die under the wheels of a bus. We can therefore rejoice that the deceased Christian is with the Lord, *'which is better by far'* (Philippians 1:23), but recognise that God ideally wants us to live until our *'time to die'* (Ecclesiastes 3:2). When Chris and I ministered in Spain a lady testified how she had come to know Christ as Saviour as 'I realised it wasn't just pie in the sky when you die. I wanted a bite now!'

Where and when

There is also a right time for healing in the sense that God may specifically show when and where it will be. He told terminally ill King Hezekiah through the prophet Isaiah,

> *'I have heard your prayer and seen your tears; I will heal you. On the third day from now you will go up to the temple of the* Lord*. I will add fifteen years to your life ... '* (2 Kings 20:5–6)

And still today God extends some people's lives after prayer. Occasionally too He promises a specific time for complete healing, as He did in the remarkable case of Nita Edwards, who was told she would be healed from paralysis on 11 February 1977 at 3.30 p.m., which is exactly what happened!

The third day

Saul of Tarsus was three days without sight but then was healed (Acts 9:9, 17–18), and it sometimes takes three days for the effects of a sickness to wear off before a person is fully well. Though we must not assume that God always does something obvious on the third day, Chris and I have often proved the scripture, *'on the third day he will restore us'* (Hosea 6:2). Nothing obvious happened when we were laying hands on one blind lady, but three days later she was descending the staircase in her house when for the first time she was able to see letters lying on her doormat.

'A Time to Heal'

This is the title of a comprehensive Church of England report on the realm of healing and wholeness, including the relation of the Church's ministry to orthodox and complementary medicine. The report was commissioned at the turn of the millennium, since which time the diocesan councils of health and healing, such as the one Christine joined, have been studying the report with the aim of encouraging its implementation in churches and parishes.

The title *A Time to Heal* is taken from Ecclesiastes 3:3. One of the questions we constantly need to ask is, 'What is it time for?' Chris once called at a hairdresser's to make an appointment, but afterwards, as she did her shopping, she grew more and more uneasy about what she had arranged. So strong was the Lord's prompting that she called at the hairdresser's again and changed the date of her appointment. When she arrived home I informed her that I had just booked an appointment with my bishop at the exact date and time that she had first arranged to have her hair permed. Since we each needed our car for these trips, we would have had to alter all our arrangements if Chris had not listened to God's voice within her.

Spiritual seasons

We do not always hear the Lord speaking so clearly, since just as there is a time for everything in the natural realm, so there is in the spiritual. Sometimes Chris and I experience a 'reaping time' when practically everyone to whom we minister is blessed in an obvious way. During other periods there is no apparent outward sign of what the Lord is doing. We have had seasons of provision where the money donated has just covered our needs: at other times we have to wait. There are seasons of attack and easier times, seasons of feasting and periods of fasting, times when our guidance is clear-cut and others when we seem to be walking in the dark. We have found we can use the lessons learned in one season to help us in the next, and, if we miss what God wants to say to us that is important, we have found He will often keep saying the same thing until it sinks in!

Testimony time

There are also particular times for particular actions. For instance there is *'a time to kill* [e.g. curse cancers] *and a time to heal'* (Ecclesiastes 3:3), *'a time to be silent and a time to speak'* (Ecclesiastes 3:7). Some Christians talk too much instead of listening, but many keep quiet when they should open their mouths. In particular, we can all share with others when we have been healed ourselves. Some remain silent because Jesus sometimes used to tell people not to mention that He had healed them (e.g. Mark 1:44), but Jesus probably said this because the time had not yet come for Him to proclaim openly that He was the Messiah (John 2:4; contrast Mark 14:61–62). He could have been strung up on a cross long before the appointed time if He had not warned people about what they might say, especially in those areas (most places) where it could have spelled danger for Him. Once He had given His Great Commission (Mark 16:15), however, there were no such restrictions, and today we need to share our testimonies.

A time to minister

We turn now to asking if there is a right time to offer healing. It is always right to pray for a sick person if the individual concerned is willing and receptive, but leaders need to know when to minister in public. There are advantages in praying for the sick in a large meeting. The united praise and prayer can be a prelude to the Lord moving powerfully in healing, so even a person who slips in at the back anonymously can benefit. But there are some advantages in private ministry too. It usually allows more time for a person to share about his or her needs and for us to minister specifically to each one.

When to minister

We believe in the regular ministry of laying-on-of-hands, but the timing will vary. The right time may be when someone has faith to be healed, like the cripple at Lystra (Acts 14:9ff.).

On the other hand, Chris and I have learned not to rush to the aid of everyone who asks us for help, even if someone is desperate or suicidal. We seek the Lord each time and He shows us when to act. We know that whenever He stops us from ministering swiftly, He has a reason. Martha and Mary must have felt annoyed and frustrated when Jesus failed to come immediately to His sick friend Lazarus. Jesus deliberately stayed in the same place for another two days (John 11:6), and by that time Lazarus had died. It was not that Jesus didn't care but because He realised a greater miracle would take place: Lazarus would be raised from the dead (John 11:43–44).

If Chris and I have sensed that a person may benefit from soaking prayer we have laid hands on him or her as soon as possible. While we are all still talking about everyday things the healing power can be flowing through. At other times the Lord has given us a physical 'nudge' when we are to begin ministry (see Question 33). He has also shown us, completely or in stages, the order of needs to be prayed about, if there are several. And we have always known, too, when to finish ministering. God may put a word into our minds, we may feel that the power has drained through our hands, or it may be obvious to one of us in some other way that it is time to end the session.

Be flexible

What is appropriate for one occasion may not be for another. In our healing services we have usually included worship, the message and the laying-on-of-hands in that order. But one summer an article about us appeared on the front page of a free regional newspaper and as a result floods of needy people came to a service of healing. As a result it seemed sensible to invite people in pain to come forward earlier than usual. Some weeks later an elderly lady wrote this to us:

> 'When you asked if anyone was in pain I told you that I had rheumatoid arthritis. I could see the Lord Jesus with His hands outstretched towards me. The next day I was getting dinner for my husband when suddenly I realised I could put my arms up to the cupboard above us and reach the salt. My husband could hardly believe his eyes. Some time has now passed and it's still the same. I feel loosened up. Thank God, this is wonderful!'

Leaders also need to be flexible about the exact manner in which to carry out the ministry. Frequently in church we have asked people to stand for this but on other occasions to kneel. Sometimes we have called people forward in groups – each group having a different need. In small gatherings we have invited everyone to form a circle while each person ministered to stands in the middle. At training days and conferences we have encouraged people to minister to each other with supervision. Sometimes we have sensed that some people present would benefit from further ministry, counselling or home visits.

Waiters and waitresses

God promises His people, *'they that wait upon the L*ord *shall renew their strength ...'* (Isaiah 40:31, AV). This does not mean that we idle away our time till the Lord heals us! We are each rather like a waiter in a restaurant, who stands still only until he has received orders. Then, at the right time, he must act on them as quickly as possible.

Meaningful silences

It is easy to think we know what God wants done when we have not waited on Him first. In some healing meetings leaders keep things moving so rapidly that they don't give the Lord a chance to speak. The most meaningful silences tend to be the ones that just arise during the worship. If leaders are sensitive to the Holy Spirit they will allow these periods to be times of waiting on the Lord in which He may give words or revelations as timely messages. Once, in one of my vicarages, those of us gathered were filled with awe as He told us to remove our footwear and kneel before Him (cf. Psalm 95:6). Then He told us we were His orchestra. Each was to play a different part but each was to come in on cue, not too soon or too late. 'Then,' He said, 'I will extract from you a beautiful melody and harmony which will resound far beyond these walls.'

Practical discussion questions

1. Can you give examples of how the Lord has been guiding you in your daily lives? Do you find it difficult to hear His voice?

2. Has anyone died in your church after having been prayed for? How do you reconcile this with having a successful healing ministry?

3. Is there opportunity in your church for testimonies by people healed through prayer? How about people from other churches too?

4. What sort of a waiter or waitress are you (Isaiah 40:31)? Do you think you need more training in listening, serving or both?

Question 17: Root Causes
How Can We Discern the Root Cause of a Sickness?

The minister of Christian healing and the complementary therapist are both concerned to find root causes. This is not always
necessary but often, once the root cause of a problem is found, it is
halfway to being solved. Even in a five-minute ministry with a
person in a healing service I have often found this approach
helpful and effective.

Underlying causes

Stress is one of the many different causes of physical conditions
and this, in turn, has many different causes: marital, occupa-
tional, financial, chemical, spiritual. When we have exhausted
all of the other possibilities the root may prove satanic, but we do
not advise always waiting until then before considering this
possibility.

A physical problem often dates back to a particular accident or
traumatic shock. Chris and I used to travel to minister healing to
people in their homes. One of the people we visited was Pam, who
lives mainly in Kensington, London, but has a holiday home at
Rustington, West Sussex. Her disease of the eyelids had been
diagnosed as medically incurable, and she feared it might ultimately lead to blindness. After we had laid hands on Pam and
prayed with her once a month for four months, she was gradually
able to come off every one of all the antibiotics and steroids she
had been taking.

Her condition then stabilised. Each time we ministered, there
was some improvement, but before we were due to visit Pam again
she would experience a slight deterioration. Once or twice she
waited longer than usual before calling upon us and at such times
her condition appeared to worsen. However, when we laid hands
on her the Lord brought her back to the point of stability she had
enjoyed before. Eventually, we traced the root cause of her
problem to a fall many years previously when she had dislocated
her neck. Once we then persisted with ministry for this she soon
found complete healing, and twenty years later she still loves to
tell everyone about it!

Four garden tools

In addition to the ministry by the Christian or the treatment by the therapist there are four particular tools used to dig up the roots, and, to make them easy to remember, we use the acronym 'GALE': Gifts, Asking, Listening and Experience. In the remainder of this chapter we are going to explore these more fully in reverse order.

The first tool: Experience – a mounting pile of wisdom

Therapists have their medical or specialist training to help them make a diagnosis, and some complementary practitioners are better at this than doctors. Some therapies are chiefly diagnostic, such as iridology, which works through the eyes, and in biofeedback the body's functions can be measured using especially designed equipment. But the ordinary Christian may have no previous experience of diagnosing. Never mind! The moment that you embark upon healing ministry you begin to gain some valuable experience. If we absorb what we learn on one occasion, we can make use of it on subsequent occasions, as the Holy Spirit reminds us of certain things (John 14:26) and as we put our experience into practice.

Emotional attitudes

I have already referred to the direct connection between physical conditions and emotional attitudes. An ulcerated colon sometimes can indicate hatred of the opposite sex. An alcoholic may have a dominating mother and a passive father. Asthma can possibly indicate a stifled cry for help. In addition there is a direct connection between emotional attitudes and spiritual ambitions. For example, a Christian who is ill or depressed may harbour guilt and become obsessed with cleanliness because he feels he has failed God. He may have a misplaced sense of duty, or constantly feel unworthy because of a false humility, forgetting that Christians are sons of God (Romans 8:15) and princes and princesses in His royal family.

The more we minister, the more we learn and the clearer will be our understanding of underlying problems. It is important we make a correct diagnosis or we may offer the wrong treatment, such as anointing with oil someone whose real need is deliverance ministry.

The second tool: Listening – with both ears wide open

Chris and I have done a lot of prayer counselling in the past and spent long periods listening to people before ministering to them. We like to think that we have one ear open to the person and the other to the Lord, so that we become aware of root causes by both taking in what the person shares and also ideas God puts into our minds (1 Samuel 3:10). Then in prayer counselling we have encouraged those with whom we are praying to relive in their imagination the accident, bereavement, shock, difficult relationship, or whatever the root cause may be, but picturing Jesus there with them. In this way the sting has been taken out of painful memories, leading to a new peace and freedom. Jesus once caused Peter, who had disowned Him three times in front of a charcoal fire (Luke 22:54–62), to relive his painful experience in front of another charcoal fire (John 21:9–17), bringing him what today we call inner healing by getting to the root of his problem.

Are we really listening?

Sometimes Christians make hasty judgements because they do not take time to listen carefully to people in need. An elderly lady once suddenly appeared to become senile, acting in a peculiar manner. Her churchgoing friends immediately began to shun her instead of listening to her. They were ready to 'push her down the slippery slope'. But there were one or two caring Christians who did listen to her and pray for her, and the result was that she was diagnosed as having diabetes. Once this was brought under control she was her usual self again, and so her so-called friends rallied around her.

The real need

What someone shares is not always his or her real need. We need to listen for what lies beneath what is said: for example, the person who says she has financial struggles may also have problems in her marriage. Some people have no difficulty naming the origin of their problems, but when there is a barrier preventing a person from experiencing peace and it is not obvious what it is, God may reveal it to us as we listen to Him. It may, for instance, be subconscious resentment because the person has been hurt by a parent or another authority figure. When there is a multiplicity of needs the usual order for ministry is first spiritual needs, next inner ones, and then physical. But, since every case is different, this order is not sacrosanct.

Listening to the body

Sometimes the person's body itself will indicate what is wrong. A vicar and his wife had coffee with Chris and me in our garden and then the vicar asked us for ministry. Chris remarked afterwards: 'I knew what he wanted prayer for before he said anything. I could tell from his body language that he was all tensed up!' Similarly on other occasions we have noticed, for instance, that someone does not wish to be touched or embraced, and this could indicate to us that the person has not been used to receiving physical affection.

Listening to the pain

When someone is in pain we may need to listen to what sort of pain it may be, for the way we should minister will differ accordingly:

1. *a worry* – we are likely to rebuke it in Jesus' name (Luke 4:39)
2. *a warning* – we look beyond the symptom to find a deeper problem
3. *a wound* – we may minister inner healing for hurts and memories.

The third tool: Asking – the questions that really matter

The questions asked to the person in need will vary according to the speciality of the one treating him or her. The osteopath may ask, 'How do you sit in relation to your computer?' The psychotherapist may ask, 'Did you have a happy childhood?' The nutritional therapist may ask, 'Do you have breakfast every day?' But each looks for root causes.

Putting things right

When Jesus asked the epileptic boy's father, *'How long has he been like this?'* (Mark 9:21), He too was looking for the root cause. The answer *'From childhood'* holds true for many conditions. However, since Jesus is the same yesterday as today (Hebrews 13:8), we can ask Him to go back into the person's yesterdays and put everything right that went wrong.

We have to be particularly sensitive if the root cause turns out to be bereavement – that is, something wrenched from the person. It may be the death of a loved one, friend, close associate or pet, an abortion or miscarriage, but also separation from a partner, friend or job, or another trauma such as rape, abuse or burglary.

Two common questions

'How did this begin?' is the question I have asked perhaps more
than any other, but just as important is, 'Have you received other
help?' The answer to this reveals other links in the chain of people
God may have used to assist the person in need, and I then
endeavour to be the next link in that chain by adding to what has
been done. On the other hand, the person may refer to questionable assistance such as from spiritists, and this, led by the Lord, I
seek to undo.

The fourth tool: Gifts – that go to the heart of the problem

Chris once asked a woman, 'What's up?' when this woman had
displayed no indication that anything was wrong; yet it transpired
that she was deeply distressed. Such intuitive gifts are often used
by some therapists and healers, and they can be valuable in
getting to the root of the problems, though they should not be
relied on too heavily.

Intuition, however, should not be confused with genuine gifts
of the Holy Spirit such as words, pictures, tongues and impressions
that the Lord can give Spirit-filled Christians when ministering.

What to pray about

One exciting thing about spiritual gifts is that God can use them
to show us just what to pray about. Albert was a parishioner who
had been seriously injured during the Second World War. Chris
and I ministered to him weekly in his home, often using soaking
prayer. Eventually his circulation would be normal again and he
would discard the medical corset he had worn since the war. One
evening before we visited him the Lord showed us a picture of an
orange. When Chris asked Albert if this meant anything to him he
burst into tears. He was remembering comrades he had seen killed
around him in Palestine, something about which he had never
previously shared. We knew that these memories should be the
focus of our prayer that evening, and afterwards he was able to
recall these events without pain. In turn, this opened the way for
his physical healing.

We shall look further at spiritual gifts in succeeding chapters.
One of these is distinguishing spirits (1 Corinthians 12:10),
which is perhaps needed more than any other gift in our
churches today, to ensure we are not unwittingly deceived by
the enemy. A Christian psychiatrist visited a man diagnosed with

schizophrenia who had been in a mental hospital for no less than fifty-two years. But the psychiatrist discerned that the man was not mentally ill at all but demon possessed. He obtained permission to minister to him, cast out the evil spirits, and the man left the hospital after fifty-two years, free and in his right mind (cf. Mark 5:15)!

God's finger

God can show us through spiritual gifts what to do or how to pray by putting His finger on the root cause(s) of a person's problem before we even begin a ministry or treatment session. But on other occasions it may not be until we have already begun the treatment or ministry that the Lord gives us insight. When we lived near Horsham, Chris and I visited Felicity, a middle-aged woman who had pain at the base of her spine as a result of a recent fall. Chris placed her hands on the affected part while I prayed aloud, but, as the ministry continued, Chris felt her hands being taken higher up the woman's back until they came to rest upon another section of her spine. 'No, *that's* where the trouble is,' Chris cried. 'No, it's not,' retorted the woman, 'the pain's lower down.' But then she added, 'Wait a minute, though. Many years ago, when I was a girl of ten, I had another fall, and then the pain *was* higher up – where your hands are now!' Once again the Lord had put His finger on the root cause of a problem.

Practical discussion questions

1. Have you or a colleague been suffering from any form of stress recently? What was the cause and what solutions are available?

2. What questions do you ask most often when ministering healing?

3. How would you minister to someone who has been bereaved in the sense of having someone or something wrenched from him or her lately?

4. What spiritual gifts have you found most useful in ministering for healing or prayer counselling? (See 1 Corinthians 12:8–10.)

Question 18: Supernatural Knowledge
How Do I Know if I Have a Message from the Lord?

Before I call upon four witnesses in reply to this question, I would like to answer two related questions which I am asked quite often: 'How do we receive God's messages?' and 'How should such messages be tested?' In each case the questioner is not referring primarily to God's messages as they are given in sermons, talks, seminars or books like this, but to gifts of the Holy Spirit such as prophecy, interpretation of tongues, words of knowledge and words of wisdom (1 Corinthians 12:8–10). These are all immensely valuable in the realms of healing and wholeness, and important means of guidance.

How God's words are manifested

Premonitions and prayer
Just as intuition is not a spiritual gift since it can be manifested by non-Christians, neither is having premonitions, though when Christians have had these – such as a warning of a plane crash – they have sometimes enabled believers to escape injury or death or to pray for those concerned in tragic incidents before those events have occurred.

Prophetic revelations
Gifts such as supernatural knowledge from God, however, are only bestowed upon committed Christians – usually Spirit-filled ones – and like the other charismatic gifts are manifested primarily for a particular purpose for a particular person at a particular time. They may come in the form of words that are self-explanatory or need explanation, in pictures that may need to be described, in fleeting impressions or convictions, in revelations seen with the eyes of the mind, in visions seen with the eyes of the body, in feelings manifested through the body, or by the action of angels.

This supernatural knowledge may arrive out of the blue, as we are waiting on the Lord in prayer or silence, or as we minister or are being ministered to. It is then usually up to us to speak out such knowledge, as it may be a message for the person receiving it but more often it is what God wants to say through him or her to someone else. Supernatural wisdom may be given too: the ability to apply knowledge. Such wisdom is very important, for these revelations need to be shared sensitively. Jesus talked at length with the woman at the well before challenging her with what had been supernaturally revealed to Him: *'you have had five husbands, and the man you now have is not your husband'* (John 4:18).

Prompted to speak

Sometimes the Lord may give someone a 'nudge' as a prompt to speak out the knowledge received, and it may not be until the Christian speaks that the purpose of God's guidance becomes clear. A lady at Hull called Shirley asked her vicar to pray that she would receive messages of knowledge. Not long after this I was leading a healing mission at their church attended by people from twelve Anglican parishes in the area, and Shirley told me of her desire. 'I feel the gift could be very useful in guiding me to pray with sick people,' she shared. Then during the Sunday morning service Shirley approached me in the ministry time and cried, 'John, I'm suddenly feeling a trembling on my lips and hands, and I've pain in my chest!' She could not understand it, but I said, 'It's the answer to your prayer! The Lord is anointing your lips for speaking and your hands for touching.' 'What about my chest pains?' asked Shirley. 'Perhaps you are meant to minister to someone with chest trouble,' I rejoined. Sure enough, when Shirley asked him, the man sitting next to her said he had pains in his chest! So, having gained the vicar's permission, she laid hands on the man for his healing.

How God's words are measured

What if there is no evidence in a meeting that a word of knowledge is from God? This sounds a reasonable question but it assumes that everything must become clear quickly, which is not always the case. We do need to *'test the spirits to see whether they are from God'* (1 John 4:1), but this does not mean pulling to pieces everything people say, or rejecting something if it is not immediately clear. However, when something someone says does not ring true to our understanding of Scripture or our past experience, that is the time gently and lovingly to question the validity of such a gift.

Clear confirmation

In particular, we need to weigh up messages when they are speaking of large or specific events (cf. 1 Corinthians 14:29). Paul says, *'you can all prophesy in turn'* (1 Corinthians 14:31), but this should be in the context of order, freedom and love. Jesus warned, *'Watch out for false prophets'* (Matthew 7:15), but some prophecies by God's people today are mixed rather than false. We need to discern when individuals have added their own desires to a genuine message from God. We also need to be cautious about giving out numbers and dates, especially in relation to people's healing. Specific words should be clearly confirmed before they are shared with the sick person.

Let's now call our first witness to how we know when it is God who is speaking through us.

The first witness: the testimony of others

The first main way you know your message is from the Lord is if other Christians tell you. For this to happen you must obviously tell someone of the possibility, even if you remain unsure of its source. One of the slogans we use in Breath is worth learning by heart:

▶ *'If you're not sure, **share!**'*

If you are uncertain about sharing it publicly, then tell it first to Christian friends whom you can trust to be caring but honest.

Extra knowledge

Very often when someone receiving ministry has shared very little, he or she has said afterwards, 'What you prayed about was exactly right.' This is because the Lord will give us extra knowledge if we ask Him, in addition to what we can acquire naturally. I shall never forget the first time I had this experience in public. I had asked for this gift because I had often used it in personal counselling but realised it could also be of tremendous value in meetings. So it came as no surprise that I soon found myself in a position where I had to use it, for that is what God will do if you ask Him for a gift: put you in a situation where you will need to use it!

It was the last evening of a mission Chris and I were leading at a Pentecostal church in Nottingham and everybody thought that the service had finished. It had lasted three hours and there had been queues for the laying-on-of-hands. Suddenly Christine had a strong anointing upon her. Her breath was being taken away and she began to gasp, while her hands were shaking violently. She realised it was the Lord's power and she wanted to say something but did not have a clue what it was. Then I heard myself speaking gently but with authority: 'The Lord's showing me there's a lady here who's deeply hurt inside. She's in need of ministry but she hasn't come forward to receive it, and the Lord wants my wife to lay hands on her.'

An elderly lady walked unsteadily forward, tears rolling down her cheeks. Chris placed her hands on her head and was led to pray a very soothing prayer asking Jesus to heal her deep hurts. After the meeting we were told, 'You wouldn't know, because you're only visiting us. But if anyone ever needed ministry for deep hurts it was that lady! For a few weeks ago her husband committed suicide. He just walked up to their garden shed and took some weedkiller.'

The second witness: the testimony of time

I have already referred to the fact that it may take time before it is clear whether a message is from the Lord. We should listen carefully to such messages. If, for example, a Christian announces that God has healed someone, then we may have to wait for medical confirmation (cf. Luke 17:14). But perhaps the message was simply that the Lord was touching the person at his or her point of need. Most prophecies are *forth*telling, giving encouragement, guidance or challenge for the moment, but some are *fore*telling, and then the obvious confirmation is whether they come to pass (Deuteronomy 18:22). There are also times when it is right to ask for a sign or 'put out a fleece' (Judges 6:37–40) – that is, to ask the Lord to provide something within a specified period of time – though at no point should we bargain with Him on terms which we have made ourselves.

The third witness: the testimony of experience

When we read *'The Lord ... said to Noah'* (Genesis 7:1), how did God speak? We are not told it was through other people or angels, though it could have been. Perhaps it was in Noah's mind. However God spoke, Noah had such experience of the Lord's voice that he did not hesitate to obey. Obviously there is danger in anyone saying 'The Lord told me' when they have little experience of closeness to Him, but we can respect those like Noah who have learned to know by experience.

Messages of wisdom

> *'And Jesus grew in wisdom and stature, and in favour with God and men.'*   (Luke 2:52)

Part of Jesus' experience of learning wisdom was to use messages of wisdom, especially when dealing with His enemies.

For example, when they watched to see if He would heal on the Sabbath, He stunned them by asking, *'Which is lawful on the Sabbath: to do good or to do evil, to save life or to kill?'* (Mark 3:4). And the message of wisdom is just the right word for the right occasion – a lovely gift which you may not know you have used until afterwards.

Other ways

There are also other ways in which we learn by experience when it is God who is speaking through us. Some people when receiving ministry are able to see in their minds details of the surgery that He is performing while it is happening. My own experience of prophecy is that first I have a few words which I then speak out. Then, like opening a packet of tissues, other words follow them, which are confirmed by other people present. And I have learned from physical signs too. If I have a burning in my knee during a healing service I speak this out and usually it transpires that the Lord is touching someone's painful knee.

The final witness: the testimony of obedience

'I was not disobedient to the vision from heaven,' declared Paul (Acts 26:19), referring to meeting Jesus on the road to Damascus. Sometimes God's message to us is that we should do something that will benefit others as well as ourselves, and in obeying what we feel He is saying we confirm the genuineness of His revelations.

Getting priorities right

I have already mentioned Albert, one of my parishioners who received soaking prayer. He was also a shop steward in the local factory. Albert used his mandolin to accompany renewal songs, but in recent months his playing had become more important to him than the Lord. One morning before going to work Albert was looking for his slippers. When he glanced up he saw in the mirror a vision of the interior of our church with people going forward for the laying-on-of-hands, himself among them. Immediately he felt God was speaking to him about his music, showing him that he must receive ministry to help him get his priorities right. The next Sunday morning he did so, and was at the same time instantly healed of a hernia.

Missing out

If you feel God is giving you something to do, do it at the first appropriate opportunity. *'We prophesy in part'* (1 Corinthians 13:9), but if the Lord gives us words we should prophesy according to the proportion of our faith (Romans 12:6). A lady at one of our conferences had an impression of a big ear but failed to mention it. Afterwards she learned that someone there had been healed in one ear but was still deaf in the other. She realised then that the Lord had not only been giving her a message of knowledge but perhaps a gift of healing too for that man. If I fail to speak out when the Holy Spirit prompts me, someone may miss out on a healing or other blessing. Alternatively, if I step out in faith and obey God, it will eventually become clear what He wants to say and do.

This even applies when people reject the message. It can still have been from God. Isaiah was told to proclaim his message even though the people's ears would become dull and their hearts heavy (Isaiah 6:10). And those who first proclaimed Christ's resurrection were met with 'buckets of cold water' from the ones to whom they went (Mark 16:13). In these cases it was only afterwards that they were proved right.

Act on the word

Sometimes we question whether something is God's message because it sounds strange. We still need to give it! A girl at one service approached a man and told him, 'I've a word from the Lord for you. It sounds very odd, but it's this: "All my triumphs are glorious" [cf. Exodus 15:1, AV].' Immediately the man burst out laughing. 'Why are you laughing?' she enquired. 'I've been trying to decide which of two cars to buy,' he replied, 'and one of them's a Triumph.'

There are few things as satisfying as knowing that you have brought a message from God and it has borne fruit. When Christine and I took a healing week in Shropshire I spoke out a prophecy that the Lord would reveal actual names and addresses of people for whom the local Christians were to pray. As I said

these words a pastor who was present heard in his mind a name
and address he had never come across. It turned out that there was
indeed an elderly couple with the name he had been given at that
address, eight miles away. That week he went to their home and
invited them to come to his church. And the Sunday after that,
they did come, and both were converted!

Practical discussion questions

1. How much should we promise sick people as we minister to them?

2. 'If you're not sure, *share!*' Have you needed to do this in your own
   ministry, and what were the final consequences of doing so?

3. Have you ever asked the Lord for a sign? And has He given signs to
   you in your everyday life that have confirmed His messages?

4. At this halfway point in the book, what have you most learned and
   gained from reading it so far?

Gifts

Question 19: Being Sure
How Do I Know if I Have a Gift of Healing?

The minister of a church where healing was frequently offered, had heart problems. This caused him every so often to come over ill in church. One day this happened while he was in the pulpit. He immediately had to sit down, and his lips turned slightly purple. 'Would someone come up and minister to me, please?' he enquired of his congregation. A lady sitting among them knew immediately that the Lord was prompting her to minister to him, but this woman had fallen out with him to the extent that they were not speaking to each other. Though the Spirit kept prompting her, she resolutely refused to leave her seat, and no one else offered to help either. After a while the minister felt a little better and continued the service. Fourteen years later that same minister told a colleague that he believed God had given the gift of healing to that woman for him. As far as I know he still suffers from the same condition.

Very precious gifts

Such gifts of healing (1 Corinthians 12:9) are very precious and are a privilege to receive and a discredit to God to refuse. Having looked in recent chapters at other spiritual gifts, which God uses to guide us in healing ministry, in this section of the book we will be mainly concerned with gifts of healing themselves: in this chapter especially in relation to Christian ministry, in the next in connection with counterfeits, and in the following one in association with other types of healing abilities. As in the last chapter, however, let me before replying to the main question endeavour to answer two related ones which I have often been asked: 'Is it necessary to be certain?' and 'What are gifts of healing?'

The value of being sure

The mysterious in Christianity can keep us humble and respect-ful and even the keenest Christians have doubts at times. But when it comes to sharing, whether our faith or God's healing, we must be *sure*. For someone who goes into the witness box and says, 'I hope so' or 'I think so' is no good as a witness. Yet, if you ask many people in our churches whether they have eternal life they will answer, 'I hope so' or 'I think so'! How different it is when we read John's first letter: *'We **know** that we have passed from death to life'* he writes (1 John 3:14, my emphasis), and the words 'we know' or 'you know' come twenty-three times. There is sometimes much emphasis too on being still (quite rightly) but the Bible says, *'Be still, and **know** . . . '* (Psalm 46:10). So the doctrine of assurance is vital. If I thought I could lose eternal life, it would not be eternal and there would be no other hope for me! But however much someone falls out with his father he remains his father's child, and I am a child of God. So the questioner is quite right in this chapter and the previous one to ask, 'How do I *know?'* because of some things we must sure.

The nature of healing gifts

And after a while some people need to know if they have had a gift of healing. I put this in the past tense because – referring for the moment to the charismatic gift manifested by Christians – no one normally knows if they have expressed such a gift until after it has gone! Remember that these gifts are not primarily for those who carry them but – like those the postman brings – for those to whom they are delivered. I do not, therefore, have a gift of healing at the moment unless, exceptionally, the very words which I am typing are the means of you, the reader, being healed. The gifts of healing operate only as God determines (1 Corinthians 12:11), and we simply pass them on.

Interestingly, healing is the only one of the supernatural gifts that St Paul puts in the plural, perhaps because there are so many different ways in which God's healing can be conveyed. I have known Christian people manifest them in all kinds of different contexts – nursing, counselling, evangelism and social work, for example – besides in the church service or prayer group. But church leaders can be looking out for those who have used these gifts on previous occasions and encourage them to take part in the healing ministry.

Ministries of healing

However, nine times out of ten that I have been asked the question at the top of this chapter, the questioner is really referring to a *ministry* of healing ('healers': 1 Corinthians 12:28, RSV). And I *do* have a *ministry* of healing right now! I have been led by the Lord to be constantly involved with sick and needy people and I have seen many of them healed. Let me, therefore, now summarise how charismatic gifts of healing can be manifested:

1. by all Christians occasionally as they share God's healing love
2. by some Christians frequently as they see they have shared a gift
3. by some Christians constantly as they lead ministry for healing.

Many ministries started simply by obeying Jesus' command to heal whenever opportunity arose, but led on from there to bigger things.

For the remainder of this chapter I will be answering the question in relation to the third type of Christian that I have listed: the one who enquires, 'How do I *know* that I have a healing ministry?' It is certainly not by putting a notice on your door and declaring you're a healer! Nor is it by completing qualifications in a training course on Christian healing, such as those Breath is able to provide. There are two answers to the question, and only two.

1. When people keep getting healed through you

A lady at Tonbridge, Kent, laid hands on a blind man and to both their astonishment she felt power surge through her and he began to see. Thereafter other sick people were healed through her ministry too.

Misunderstandings about ministries

But some people are heard to exclaim, 'Surely God will give me any gifts He wishes me to have!' I said these words once when told I would benefit from speaking in tongues. But this is a misunderstanding. God wishes to give eternal life to people, but He does not do this casually: they have to accept it. And ministries don't usually drop into our hands either: it is as we act that we see things happen.

Another misunderstanding is that Christian leaders should be good at every ministry, including healing. One vicar in Warwickshire was on the verge of a nervous breakdown because his congregation expected him to be constantly manifesting every gift in the book!

Then there is the way people interpret signs. Sometimes someone says to Chris and me, 'I've a tingling in my hands. Does that mean God is calling me into a healing ministry?' We then reply, 'Hold on. It may be the first sign, but there's a lot more to it than that.' We go on to remind the person of all the suffering we had to go through before our ministry came to fruition, as described in *It Hurts to Heal*. Not everyone will have the same sort of preparation, but much confirmation is required before you can assume you have a healing ministry – especially constant healings! However, when a lady at Barking spoke of a tingling in her hands she added that she had experienced this every time she had observed the laying-on-of-hands during the previous ten years. So we encouraged her to launch into ministry soon, as that was obviously what God was calling her to do.

Links in God's chain
Remember that a healing ministry is not only for restoration but also for:

1. the prevention of disease, through whatever means God chooses
2. improvement in the person's quality of life and total condition
3. re-creation of bodily organs, such as new limbs, eyes or teeth.

High success in a particular area of healing may mean someone has a ministry for that area, but we are each only one link in God's chain, so we must each play our part, or the chain breaks and God must find someone else. Your ministry belongs to Him, not you. A Christian leader who has specially promoted the value of vitamins once declared, 'When I realised that I was not the Holy Spirit, all the strain was taken out of my healing ministry!' (cf. Acts 3:12).

Preparation and observation
There is no preparation of the sick in the Gospels and yet there is plenty of preparation of the ministers of healing. The Lord often

tells me to 'be aware and observant', and one way we prepare is by observing others with ministries who are experienced in this area. A man was watching as I was ministering deliverance in Wales to a psychiatric nurse who had been involved in the occult. Afterwards he shared, 'I have never seen that done before. I have learned a lot today.'

All the time and at the time

Those with healing ministries are never really 'off duty'. A lady found herself ministering to an ill woman in a superstore, another in a ladies' cloakroom, another to a person who felt faint on a bus. Some Christians, including those who are housebound, have been led into ministries of intercession, while others pray regularly for the absent sick. A Liverpool man with bowel trouble was healed at the exact time he was prayed for in Kent. A Glasgow woman felt her depression lift as Breath people prayed for her at East Grinstead.

2. When people keep telling you it's true

This is the only other way you can be absolutely sure that God has given you a ministry of healing. A couple were leaving church one evening when someone asked them for healing ministry. On another occasion someone else asked them for the same thing. Each time the request came without warning, it concerned knee trouble, and the afflicted person was healed through their prayers. It wasn't long before the couple concluded, through what people were saying, that the Lord wished to use them in a ministry to people's knees. A girl I knew had a ministry to migraines. And at Woking there was a man who had a ministry to backs, and who frequently witnessed people's backs getting healed as he laid hands on their feet and the shorter of their legs grew to the size of the other. Since back trouble is so common, he literally had his hands full. But he was proving the truth of Psalm 146:8, which can be rendered, 'He straightens the backs of those who are bent.'

Public healing ministries

If you reckon you are being called to a *public* healing ministry, God may confirm this by ensuring that the first person you touch in public is obviously healed. But it's important that you don't just rely on the first test that people keep getting healed through you, but that you should also obtain plenty of confirmation from other people. If you inform your pastor about the possibility, he will be

able to tell you whether you can use your ministry in his church or
if you must look elsewhere. The other necessity is that you acquire
some form of training. You should find that this book and *Six Keys
to Healing* can help you with this, though of course there is no
substitute for actually attending a training course where you can
minister to other people yourself with supervision.

The Welshman Stephen Jeffreys had a notable healing ministry
and thousands were blessed through it, especially those suffering
from rheumatoid arthritis. But one day at a big meeting in South
Africa where hundreds were being healed, instead of saying,
'Come to Jesus', he said, 'Come to *me*.' From then on his
congregations dwindled and his ministry had little effect. He died
of rheumatoid arthritis.

Practical discussion questions

1. How do you know you have eternal life? (Revelation 3:20; 1 John
   3:24)

2. How can spectators of the healing ministry become participants?

3. Chris and I also have a joint ministry. What are the particular
   benefits of going out to heal or deliver in twos? (Luke 10:1)

4. Are there Christians in your church or group who would benefit
   from the specific ministry of a healing home or retreat centre?

Question 20: Genuine Healing
Isn't All Healing from God?

The answer is yes if it is genuine, but no if it is counterfeit. A
Christian man once remarked to me, 'I cannot understand why
some people think some healings are from the devil. What has he
got to gain by healing people?' But remember Satan's strategy is to
get us there 'almost but not quite' (Acts 26:18). It suits his purposes
when he can sometimes deceive us with a measure of false healing
to prevent us from enjoying the wholeness that God plans for us.

Conflict

Now in healing ministry the job satisfaction is high, but one way
that Satan would rob us of this is by oppressing those involved.

They are also likely to get attacked in the areas in which they are most used. That is why so many of us with ministries of healing have fallen sick. If you are involved in a particular project for the Lord, you may find yourself under satanic attack: before, during or afterwards. But take heart!

> *'The reason the Son of God appeared was to destroy the devil's work.'* (1 John 3:8)

Although the enemy oppresses us and as individuals we are sometimes defeated, as an army we are victorious and on the winning side (Colossians 2:15).

Counterfeits

Nevertheless, there are counterfeit healings, counterfeit gifts and counterfeit ministries (1 Timothy 4:1). It is not that Satan himself always deliberately plans these, but he uses them to draw people away from God, as they do not include the true healing that God provides.

Experts and forgers

Between 1994 and 1998 there took place the largest counterfeiting money scam that had so far occurred in Britain. On both the Isle of Wight and the mainland huge amounts of twenty-pound notes were printed and distributed, and they were so like the genuine article that they even had identical watermarks and imprints. Only experts and the forgers themselves could easily detect the difference. The same consequence has occurred with counterfeit works of art.

In the spiritual world the forgers are the devil's agents and the 'experts' are those Christians who manifest the gift of discerning spirits (1 Corinthians 12:10), something we shall refer to at greater length in our discussion of Questions 25–30. For Satan's name was once Lucifer (lightbearer), and he can easily masquerade as an angel of light (2 Corinthians 11:14). Nobody today counterfeits half-crowns, for only what is usable and valuable is worth forging, and this is also true of the genuine gifts of the Spirit. Christians who were once spiritualists have told how they had a counterfeit gift for every true one, and we must not be deceived into accepting false routes of healing. The Bereans *'examined the Scriptures ... to see if what Paul said was true'* (Acts 17:11).

One of the characteristics of counterfeit healing is that it is likely to wear off in a genuine Christian healing atmosphere. A lady with a physical problem received healing at a spiritualist church and her condition cleared up. Some time later she became a Christian and immediately all her symptoms reappeared. Then she was given laying-on-of-hands with prayer in Jesus' name, and this time her physical problem was cured completely and permanently.

Cults

A large number of people have become mentally ill after joining sects and cults like the Moonies and Scientology, and we believe that counterfeit healing can be conveyed through similar groups.

Unhelpful sources

Yet it is partly the Church's fault that people are turning to unhelpful sources for healing, because in the past we have not made known that this ministry is on offer, and even now there is a tendency among some churches to do it as quietly as possible.

A cartoon once portrayed a scene in mid-ocean. Several bedraggled survivors from a shipwreck were tightly clinging to a raft as it surmounted the huge waves, but one of them was looking hopeful and pointing. The caption underneath read 'We're saved! Here comes the *Titanic!*' Thousands of people are today looking to sinking ships for healing, some because they are desperate and ignorant of God.

More harm than good

The whole area of the occult has in the experience of Chris and myself done people more harm than good, even when they may have experienced physical healings through it. While white witchcraft aims among other things to heal using herbs and potions, we view the results as counterfeit. And although there is much more of an open and caring attitude among New Agers than among some of the older sects like Jehovah's Witnesses and Mormons, we see the tendency to invoke spiritual entities by chanting, and the use of 'magic' in reciting certain words or following certain procedures, very much as danger areas for the Christian Church (see Ephesians 2:2).

Many years ago a girl called Melanie was a member of one of my church youth groups. She had been brought up in a Christian home. Some years later Christine and I heard that Melanie had joined a house group near where she lived. It was not a Christian group but Melanie was overwhelmed with the love and care of those who befriended her there. It transpired that it was a New Age type of group, which gave people such as Melanie opportunities to share and discuss about their everyday concerns. It appeared in fact to do for Melanie what Christian groups had failed to do, and at that time she had no interest in the things of the Lord.

Then she was introduced to a local church and invited to another group. Again there was love and care and sharing, but only then did Melanie realise what she had been missing. The New Age group seemed hollow in comparison. Melanie was baptised in the Spirit, and is today a keen believer and married to a Christian husband.

Clusters

Counterfeit healing can also be found in the world of alternative medicine. We have already seen how many therapies are neutral in themselves and can often be the context in which the Lord brings genuine healing, especially through those that come under the banner of complementary medicine. But we've also noted how some therapists do not just practise a particular discipline but are involved in clusters of practices.

Just a hobby
Here we must keep things in perspective. John Richards, an Anglican vicar at the forefront of the Church's healing ministry, has pointed out that the devil's work in alternative medicine is just a hobby compared to his main work in the church. If he can get his agents into Parochial Church Councils and deacons' meetings, he can much more easily disrupt, divide and discourage the people of God! But alternative medicine by its very nature remains a minefield, and that's why PACT is giving a lead to Christians in this area.

Disturbing situations
In just a few cases individuals have told me how, when they went for the first time to a qualified practitioner expecting to benefit from a recognised therapy, that practitioner without warning began to do other things which were nothing to do with the treatment and which caused the Christian client to feel disturbed.

In my answers to Questions 24 and 25 I will look at how these concerns can be avoided, but it reveals why some believers only feel safe if they are able to consult Christian therapists like those on our register – though we have never felt that practitioners should *only* be Christians.

When ministering to people who have been disturbed after visiting therapists, and when we are not sure how helpful or otherwise the practitioner has been, Chris and I pray for discernment about the situation, and, if we are still unsure, we set the person concerned free in Jesus' name from any harm that may have been done and ask the Lord to maintain in the person what is helpful in His sight.

Of course, doctors, therapists, even Christians, make mistakes in diagnosis and treatment. But when the help given is beneficial to the person, is not contrary to the Scriptures, and is acceptable to Christian leaders, it is probably genuine and worth receiving.

Practical discussion questions

1. Why are more people believed to be healed through the prayers of others than their own? (Luke 10:1; James 5:14–16)

2. Give examples of how Satan gets us almost there but not quite.

3. Have you had any experience of counterfeit healings among your friends? Were these recognised as such by the people concerned?

4. What might you do if you believed a genuine mistake had been made by someone who is regularly treating you or ministering to you?

Question 21: Different Gifts

What Do I Say to a Non-Christian Who Claims to Have Healing Gifts?

'Tell me about it', would be my immediate response. Jesus said, *'Do not judge, or you too will be judged'* (Matthew 7:1), but there is a temptation among some Christians to judge others before they've learned the facts. It will soon become clear from what is said if:

1. the person is truly a Christian, though we did not realise this
2. the person uses questionable healing which may be counterfeit
3. the person is rather using natural or psychic gifts of healing.

If I discovered the person was not a committed believer I would gently but firmly explain the differences with Christian healing and invite him or her to a Christian meeting. When a group of people who called themselves spiritualist healers came along to some of our meetings they were amazed at how much more Jesus offered, and they were also surprised at the release of power which was so evident.

Spiritual healers

In Appendix 1 I attempt to explain several of the different terms used in relation to healing. It is important to grasp what people mean by particular terms so that we all understand where they are coming from. And while most Christians prefer not to use the term 'healer' of themselves, non-Christians who believe they exercise healing gifts now almost always call themselves spiritual healers.

Healing organisations

'Spiritual healing', or simply 'Healing', is the term most often used by all kinds of people for healing through laying-on-of-hands. This is the term used too by the British Confederation of Healing Organisations, which encompasses more than a dozen of these societies including the very large National Federation of Spiritual Healers. This last organisation provides extensive courses teaching about healing and how to develop healing gifts. It also offers the most extensive referral system to healers. While it contains a growing number of Christians, it includes a copious number of people with spiritist leanings, a broad array of natural and psychic healers, and many who are New Age adherents. The healers are often isolated individuals and quite frequently unaccountable to any other body.

Higher up the scale

An important principle that we observe in PACT is that the higher up the scale we go of body, mind and spirit, the more cautious we all need to be. If I fracture my arm and it is operated on by an orthopaedic surgeon I'm not concerned about his personal life or beliefs as long as he knows his job! He may be a consultant of a different race, colour or creed, he may be a spiritualist or even a witch for all I know. I may feel it right to ask others to pray for me, and perhaps I'll claim the Lord's protection (Psalm 91), but that's all. However, if someone is to treat my *mind* – such as through psychotherapy or hypnotherapy – I shall want to know more about the therapist first. And if I am offered what he or she is calling *spiritual* healing I shall have far more questions to ask about this before I agree to it. In fact, as a Christian I personally would only be prepared to receive actual healing *therapy* from other believers.

But this does not mean we should reject all non-Christian healers. A woman who discovered she had healing gifts offered her services to nine different churches. All without exception declined to give her a welcome, most telling her that she was working for the devil. Sadly she was accepted by a spiritualist church, which she joined as she was ignorant of the dangers from a spiritual point of view.

Natural healers

'Natural healing' may refer to three types of physical restoration:

1. healing resulting after injury when the wound heals naturally
2. healing resulting from release of energy within someone's body
3. healing resulting from using natural means/substances, e.g. exercise/herbs.

Since God has made our bodies we welcome natural healing but see it as insufficient for every need. And we have already seen that the term may be used too for what is really a supernatural counterfeit.

It is the second meaning listed that concerns us most here. We have noted too that complementary practitioners may also be known as natural therapists, because their treatments involve a release of energy and they use natural remedies, and so they are 'natural healers'.

God-given or evil?

But what of those non-Christians who claim to have natural gifts of healing? Some Christians believe such abilities must have come into the world at the Fall of the human race (Genesis 3:22–24), so are part of the evil in the world, and should be rejected. In contrast we and other Christian people believe that, since God foreknew individuals would sin and be sick (Romans 8:29–30), at creation He put into our bodies the potential for healing, including in some people such natural gifts as would enable them to heal the sick. You must make your own decision about which of these is correct.

The natural and psychic abilities that some people have today in this connection are, we believe, (like complementary therapies) to be regarded as God-given and neutral, able to be used for good or evil. A number of natural healers with these gifts are now taking posts in hospitals, and scientific research has included evidence of their success, so they cannot be ignored by Christian people.

Knowledge and healing

It is abundantly clear to Bible-believing Christians that God has given both natural and supernatural knowledge. Natural knowledge is obtained through learning and common sense, but in some people it is also obtained through intuition and premonitions. Christians who are given supernatural knowledge recognise this as something God gives them other than by normal natural or psychic processes. Now compare knowledge with healing. Isn't it reasonable that God should have given this ability in both natural and supernatural ways too? And just as some people are naturally more knowledgeable, so some are naturally more able to bring healing. Again that which is genuinely supernatural healing from God is only manifested by believers, but *non*-Christians may have natural healing abilities.

How does natural healing take place?

Usually people who find they are able in some way to make others better offer this gift informally and may then be trained to use it in more formal and professional contexts as healing therapists. Our experience in talking to some of them is that many view their gift with no religious connotations or occult ones either. Often, however, they are respectful of the Church's healing ministry, and those who are neither Christian nor New Age in the sense of being 'governed by energy' are, nevertheless, almost always aware that the ability is not something they have manufactured but has come from 'outside' of them. Some may be trained in reiki (pronounced *raykee*), where a therapist gently places hands unintrusively in a sequence of positions covering the whole body. But Christians often prefer healing ministry to this, so those

Christians who practise it most are usually those who have been trained in reiki before becoming believers and who afterwards incorporate it into their ministries.

Natural healers sometimes pray, but usually in silence place their hands in the energy field around the person or actually touch the person in need. While a release of power and healing can result from the first method, we prefer the added value of touch described in response to Question 8. Likewise some ministering Christians only place their hands *near* a person, but many people need to *feel* the touch actually on some part of the body. That way they feel more loved and valued, and it's the way Jesus did it (e.g. Luke 4:40).

How should we react to a natural healer?

Ian Cowie describes the positive line of the Edinburgh Christian Fellowship of Healing:

> 'Join in our Bible study and prayer life. Then, if we feel that it is right, we may call on you to help.'

He explains that if these healers left disgusted, the fellowship were spared problems. If the healers joined in, and their natural gifts were used by the Holy Spirit, they gained valuable helpers.

One Sunday afternoon Chris and I were at home when our doorbell rang. A middle-aged woman stood there. 'I hope that you don't mind me calling round,' she said, 'but I only live in the next street and I've heard that people get healed through you. I've found it's happening with me too. I touch them and they keep getting better.' We invited Fiona in and she shared how she'd had this ability for some time. She was not a practising Christian, but she wondered if we could make use of her gift. She added, 'I tried the Spiritualist Church near here, but I soon realised that God didn't live there!' Under no circumstances were we going to invite Fiona to minister with us at our healing services, but we gladly invited her to them. When such natural healers also come to know Jesus, He can add His supernatural gifts to their natural ones – *then* they can minister.

Psychic healers

Christians will be even more cautious about these. We accept that God brings true healing through some natural healers who also use intuitive abilities when treating sick people and giving advice.

Dangers to avoid

We do *not* accept psychic healing if:

1. it is in reality simply another term for using spiritist phenomena;
2. it involves contacting 'earth-forces' – just as harmful as 'spirit-forces';
3. it uses mind over matter alone to influence bodily restoration.

(Some psychic healers concentrate their 'combined thoughts' on a person or place with the intention of altering the situation.) Ian Cowie is right in *Across the Spectrum* when he concludes that someone who follows the Lord will be given such psychic elements as are needed, but those who develop psychic sensitivity on its own are in real danger, and many books on 'How can I be a healer?' are 'dangerous ego trips' (p. 70).

Two-level ministry

However, many Christians with healing ministries probably do them on both levels. On the psychic level we have techniques to learn, potential to be developed, and we need to be in a fit and healthy state, with the energy flowing smoothly. On the spiritual level we are not concerned about techniques but our relationship with God, not mind-development so much as spiritual development, and God can still use us when we're at the end of our tether and feeling low!

If we do not accept that God uses us at both levels, there is the danger that, while healings go on happening, we do not notice if we are slipping spiritually. This seems to be what happened at Corinth, where there were plenty of spiritual gifts but division and wrong living (1 Corinthians 1:7 and 10). God is looking for *rounded* ministries.

Other healers

In common with most believers we cannot accept healing ministered in the name of another god. We do welcome dialogue with people of other faiths, and we are able to work with them on certain levels. But we cannot worship their gods, even if like

Muslims they only believe in one god, for our healing prayers must always be in the name of the Trinity or in the name of Jesus (e.g. Acts 3:6), and the only way to know God as Father is through Christ (John 14:6).

Jewish healers

The one exception is Jews who bring healing in the name of Yahweh (Jehovah, the Lord). Obviously we would rather they became Messianic Jews, such as one Jewish osteopathy student, whom Chris and I asked how he became a Christian. His reply was simple: 'When I realised that the revelation was incomplete, I embraced Christianity.' But people such as Elijah brought healing in the Lord's name without knowing the Messiah (1 Kings 17:22), and so can some Jews today.

Angelic healers

A man once fell over a cliff and landed on a ledge, badly injured. He later told how two angels had appeared to him and carried him back to the top of the cliff, placing him in a spot where he would easily be found. Then they vanished. The man was discovered shortly afterwards and taken by ambulance to the nearest hospital, where he recovered.

Practical discussion questions

1. Reading this chapter, have you changed your mind about anything?

2. Discuss the alternatives that physical restoration accomplished through the aid of natural healers is either God-given or evil.

3. How would you welcome a visitor to your group who said he or she was constantly healing people but was not a practising Christian?

4. Have you had any experience of the ministry of angels? (Hebrews 1:14)

SECTION 8

Therapies

Question 22: Questionable Origins
Doesn't Acupuncture Come from Eastern Religions?

The brief general answer to this frequently asked question is no!

Whenever someone asks this it probably indicates a real concern – perhaps even a fear – that to be involved with such a therapy would be wrong for the Christian and possibly even dangerous. There is once again the idea that it could lead to a person becoming embroiled with evil powers. Now it is right that we should be cautious about therapies because we need to test these to see if they are from God (1 John 4:1), but the person who is enquiring about acupuncture in this way has probably received some incorrect teaching, made some inconsistent judgements, and consequently arrived at some inaccurate conclusions.

Incorrect teaching

A good number of Christian books and teachers have asserted that acupuncture should be rejected by the Church because it has been closely associated with Eastern religions, and a few Christian agencies have listed books on acupuncture under 'The Occult'. This in turn has resulted in much confusion and misunderstanding.

The roots of acupuncture
It is true that this form of medicine has flourished in China for centuries and the culture in that region has been dominated by religions such as Hinduism, Buddhism, Taoism and Confucianism, all of which hold many beliefs which differ from those of Christianity. But acupuncture has been used for at least 5,000 years. It is older, therefore, than Taoism. It is also obviously much older than the New Age movement. So in itself it is neither Taoist

nor is it New Age, but a neutral therapy that should be distin-
guished from these. Neither is it a 'spiritualist art', as some people
have suggested.

The ancient Chinese discovered and made use of acupuncture,
and they may have had a scientific understanding of how it works.
However, over thousands of years it has been influenced by each
current philosophy and religion, and people have interpreted it in
the light of their beliefs. A popular teaching still followed today is
that the source of all life is the *Tao* (the way), that the whole
cosmos (universe) is interrelated, and that we remain healthy by
attuning ourselves to the balance of the cosmos. These ideas are
not wholly compatible with Christianity, but because we reject
this philosophy we do not have to reject acupuncture.

Professor Malcolm Stemp has been training students in homeopathy and acupuncture for many years, and a number of them
have become Christians through his ministry. He has pointed out
that some of the understanding of ancient Chinese medicine was
in advance of modern science, such as their accurate ideas about
the circulation of the blood.

And Rachel Temple has shown how one ancient Chinese
medical book prophesied, 'There is to come a great messenger of
God, a Saviour of men. He will come in the West and his teaching
will overshadow the earth' – Jesus! Therefore, while such works as
these may be written off by some Christians because they are
occult in origin, we can make use of what is good in Chinese
literature. Similarly we can make use of what is good in Traditional Chinese Medicine, and acupuncture is one of the good
fruits that it has produced.

The roots of other therapies
The same principles can be applied to all the other therapies. We
need to distinguish carefully between the therapy and the culture
in which it has developed, between the therapy and occult
practices, and between the therapy and the particular practitioner.
Jesus did not say, 'By their *roots* you will know them' but by their
fruits (Matthew 7:20).

Christian origins
Some of these therapies were discovered by Christian people.
Osteopathy, for example, was initiated during the late nine-
teenth century by Dr Andrew Still, the son of an American
Methodist minister. And the men who founded the British School

of Osteopathy in London were also instrumental in founding two Bible colleges. Other therapies have been wrongly attributed by some Christians to questionable origins. Bach Flower Remedies (see p. 84) are said by some to have been discovered by using mediumistic powers, but Dr Edward Bach gave thanks to God for all that he had discovered, and he regarded Jesus Christ as his personal mentor in all of it.

Controversial origins

One of the most controversial therapies in the eyes of certain Christians is homoeopathy. This is in some ways surprising, as during the early part of the twentieth-century homoeopathy was very much in the hands of Christian people, and it is the only therapy – apart from Christian healing – to regard and emphasise the doctrine of original sin as part of its philosophy (Romans 5:12). But one argument is that homoeopathy is another therapy launched in questionable circumstances, since its modern founder, Dr Samuel Hahnemann, is believed to have been a Freemason. Yet Alan Crook points out that in Hahnemann's time it was routine for all brilliant and original thinkers to become Masons, and this was not then perceived as being in conflict with Christian beliefs. And is it fair to discredit a whole system by discrediting its inventor? Actually Hahnemann was not in reality the inventor of homoeopathy, but he organised it into a systematic and workable therapy. He subsequently suffered chaos and misfortune as a result of persecution by the medical and pharmaceutical professions.

Inconsistent judgements

When Christian people are considering whether to make use of a particular therapy one principle we recommend is that they look primarily at the nature of the therapy, not at how it was founded. This is not only because of the incorrect teaching that I have summarised but because the judgements we make can be inconsistent.

Is it consistent to write off a therapy as wrong because it began in questionable circumstances, when we Christians take for granted a number of other things whose origins are just as questionable?

Things we take for granted

Take the customs we use at Christmas, such as decorating a tree or hanging mistletoe. Many of these practices had pagan origins, but the early Church in its wisdom 'baptised them into Christ'. In place of decorating the oak tree in honour of the old god Odin they would decorate the fir tree in honour of the birth of Jesus. Or how about the days of our week? Do we Christians cease to call one day 'Thursday' because it was originally named after the god Thor? Or take the months of the year: March was named after Mars, the god of war. Even the greatest of all our Christian festivals, Easter, is called by that title after the ancient goddess Eostre.

To be really consistent, if we reject a therapy because of its origins we must do the same with orthodox Western medicine and cease going to the doctor! The reason I say this is because orthodox medicine has some of its roots in paganism, and Hippocrates was far from being a Christian. The Hippocratic Oath which doctors take originally began thus:

> 'I swear by Apollo the physician, and Aesculapius, and by Health and Allheal, and all the gods and goddesses, that, according to my ability and judgement, I will keep this Oath and this stipulation.'

Later Sir Isaac Newton, to whom modern medical science owes a good deal, was involved in the occult for a substantial period. Should we reject all medical discoveries because of this fact?

I am not suggesting that origins are not interesting or some-times important, but that no therapy should be judged *on origins alone.* So if you do not appreciate all that you can read about Dr William H. Fitzgerald who rediscovered a Chinese method of therapy in Connecticut, America, that is not enough to reject reflexology. If a medical herbalist dabbles in 'way-out' New Age philosophies, that is not enough for the Christian to reject medical herbalism. If some psychotherapy schools teach ideas that are in conflict with Christian philosophy – unlike say the Westminster Pastoral Foundation, which has a Christian (Methodist) basis – that is not enough to reject psychotherapy as a valid therapy for Christians.

Good out of evil
But 'Can anything good come from the East?' some will ask, echoing Nathanael's words about Nazareth (John 1:46). Not only did the wise men who worshipped the child Jesus come from the East but so did Jesus Himself! Eastern origins – however

questionable – should not prevent us from using acupuncture any more than from being treated by an Eastern surgeon. Otherwise we are certainly being inconsistent, and perhaps hypocritical too, in our choices.

In making use of therapies which have questionable origins we are simply acknowledging the Christian experience that God can bring good out of evil (cf. Romans 12:21). The greatest example of this is when He took one of the cruellest forms of execution then known – the cross – and turned it into a symbol of our faith by both enduring its torture and rising from the dead (Hebrews 12:2).

Inaccurate conclusions

It is inevitable that Christians who frequently tend to follow incorrect teaching and who make inconsistent judgements will come to inaccurate conclusions. I do not condemn these people but I hope they will think again in the light of prayer and experience. It's easy to slot what we don't understand into neat compartments but it's dangerous to limit the extent of what God can do, and not a light thing to reject something that He has genuinely provided.

For centuries some Christians have come to the conclusion that something is not of God when subsequent generations of Christians have accepted it as from Him. Even radio waves were thought to be occult at one time and also, much earlier, were knives and forks! If the person who first made the light bulb (Thomas Edison) was pagan and dabbled with an ouija board, are we to use light bulbs?

We can use the treatment provided through some therapies without ascribing to all of the associated philosophy. We shall want as Christians to ask other questions, but origins need not worry us.

East and West

They certainly do not worry many Christians in the East. One example is the largest church in the world, the Full Gospel Church at Seoul, South Korea. There thousands of people worship several times on a Sunday, many cannot wait to begin the services before praying aloud, healings take place at an associated venue called Prayer Mountain, and hundreds of missionaries are sent to the West. Yet many people in that church use acupuncture as frequently as we go to our GP. Some carry around their own sets of needles and use them for First Aid, such as for a headache. They are puzzled that in the West there is talk of 'deliverance from acupuncture'. We need to be careful that we do not seek to impose our Western culture on those who are happily serving God in a different way.

Root and fruit

There is one other objection that we must consider which some Christians make with regard to origins of therapies. While we teach that the Lord wants us to discern something by its *fruit* rather than its *root* (Matthew 7:20), they sometimes point to verse 17 of the same passage where He clearly reminds us that *'a bad tree bears bad fruit.'* Does this not mean, they argue, that if a therapy originated in 'bad circumstances' it will inevitably produce 'bad fruit'? My reply to this is twofold:

1. However bad the circumstances were in which the therapy was discovered, those circumstances were not the therapy. The therapy can still have been a 'good tree', and will produce good fruit.

2. Although good trees produce good fruit and bad trees bad, it's possible for good fruit to appear now where the bad trees once flourished. Once again we place more stress on the nature of the therapy and the good or bad practices that the practitioner is involved in, rather than making judgements according to origins. In our discussion of a later question (24) we shall consider how to examine the fruit.

Practical discussion questions

1. How can we be sure we receive accurate and reliable teaching about complementary therapies that will aid us as Christians?

2. Which particular ideas and philosophies of Eastern religions are in line with Christian teaching and which ones are not?

3. What lessons can we learn from the origins of therapies such as osteopathy, homoeopathy, aromatherapy and acupuncture?

4. What other examples can we give of things which can be 'baptised into Christ', and of how good can be brought out of evil?

Question 23: Homoeopathic Remedies

Are not Homoeopathic Remedies Too Diluted to Be Effective?

Before we can answer this question we must understand more about homoeopathy, for Proverbs 18:1 in the Living Bible states,

'What a shame! How stupid to decide without knowing the facts!'

I shall devote the whole of this chapter to this powerful treatment that once was particularly in Christian hands and is still a favourite therapy with the long-living members of the British Royal Family. (For a fuller and more detailed consideration of the subject read Alan Crook's excellent book *A Christian's Guide to Homoeopathy*.) So far we have seen how this energy medicine is based on the idea that like cures like, and that whatever questions Christians have about Hahnemann we can accept homoeopathy as God given. As it does not match remedies to diseases but to someone's overall needs it is difficult to test in a general way, such as by using the double blind placebo controlled test. But its huge success with children, animals and unconscious people indicates that its benefits are not purely the results of placebo, and should be taken very seriously. It is popular with many people, but controversial for some Christians.

How it works

Homoeopathy is another whole person remedy. People's symptoms are regarded as attempts by the body to heal itself. When a substance capable of producing a similar group of symptoms to a disease is used as a medicine, it strengthens the person's defence mechanism. If the wrong medicine is prescribed, the patient will not respond. A similar principle underlies the orthodox practice of immunisation, but in homoeopathy the remedy will *precisely* match the patient's condition, stimulating the body gradually to build up immunity.

Other examples of orthodox procedures comparable to homoeopathic ones include digitoxin – which can cause heart irregularities but also treat heart defects – and chemotherapy, which can both cause and treat tumours. Where the body has the capacity to heal

itself, homoeopathy can both speed this process and bring about
the cure. In other cases, as long as the causes of the problems
are found, the homoeopathic treatment can prevent any further
deterioration.

Advantages over orthodox medicine

1. Diagnosis is not essential in homoeopathy, although the
   remedy which is prescribed is based on the totality of the
   symptoms.
2. The cost of homoeopathic prescriptions is very small, and
   often the first prescription is all that is needed for permanent
   cure.
3. There is no danger of overdosing, dependence, addiction or
   side-effects. Children have swallowed too much of the prescribed substance without ill effects.
4. The homoeopathic medicines are tested only on human
   volunteers.

Examples from Materia Medica

The *Materia Medica* is a library of remedies, methods and uses in
homoeopathy that records effects on every tissue and organ in the
body. The list of remedies includes, for example:

Aconite:	for fear, anxiety, mental illness
Arnica:	for shock and physical bruising
Camomile:	for anger and violent tempers
Ignatia:	can bring peace and contentment

The law of cure

This is relevant to some other therapies as well. A remedy works
from the top downwards, from within outwards, from major to
minor organs, and in reverse order of appearance of symptoms.
We shall feel emotionally better before we feel physically better,
and if, for example, a rash is followed by fever and vomiting,
vomiting will stop first, then the fever will subside, and last of all
the rash will clear.

A spiritual medicine

When Hahnemann uses the word 'spiritual' in his writings it is in
the sense of 'non-material and dynamic', and not in any religious
sense. Christians should not therefore write off the therapy

because of its use of the word. In Romans 14:1–5 Paul refers to those who abstain from meat that had unclean associations as 'weak in the faith', and says those who are strong in faith eat anything. It's probably Satan who has sown the idea in some people's minds that to 'feed' on homoeopathic remedies is wrong. Sir Alexander Fleming discovered penicillin but was also a Freemason – should we then refuse antibiotics?

Training and treatment

Clinical use of the therapy is learned in a minimum of five years – beware of short cuts such as use of the pendulum. A case history may take one and a half to two hours to obtain from each patient. Rudolf Steiner's brand is not true homoeopathy, and the biochemic system of medicine tries to simplify homoeopathy when it attempts to pinpoint various deficiencies but does not find the root cause. Divination and astrology form no part of true homoeopathy as it is taught in either the primary training colleges or the textbooks.

Tried and tested

During 1991 a *British Medical Journal* survey conducted 68 homoeopathic trials and in 1997 a meta-analysis of 89 trials was published in *The Lancet.* All concluded that homoeopathy was more than placebo. Recent studies at the Royal London Homoeopathic Hospital found that the commonest reason patients attend is dissatisfaction with orthodox medicine (63 per cent), while 31 per cent objected to drugs on principle, and 38 per cent wished to reduce their dosage of orthodox medication. Some people respond better to homoeopathy than others, but these facts indicate it is a safe holistic therapy that is well worth pursuing.

How the remedies are prepared

Homoeopathy was originally criticised for being too scientific (!). The medicine of the early nineteenth century, before the molecular and atomic theories were formulated, was empirical. More recently, the therapy has been criticised for not being scientific enough. The exact mode of action is not yet known. Doctors and Christians alike often, therefore, find it difficult to believe that a remedy is effective if it is so diluted that it contains no molecules. Some Christians also conclude that there must be something magic or satanic about the whole potentisation process and its results. They wonder again whether the sometimes unexplained forces behind this process are ultimately of the devil rather than of the Lord. But what is the truth behind the tiny pills that many of us take?

Sequence of dilution

There is nothing obscure about preparing homoeopathic remedies. They begin as tinctures made from specific substances, extracted from ordinary plants such as daisies. The basic substance is immersed in alcohol and water for a few days, then strained. There follows a solution of dilution in an alcohol and water mixture. Each stage includes a thorough shaking. The whole process these days is normally done by factory machine and the tablets are mass-produced. So there is nothing occult in it. Could the shaking of such substances about a hundred times turn what is material into an immaterial essence? And if it could, why should this force necessarily be evil? How can a process which simply involves prolonged shaking of the homoeopathic solution be a means of incorporating evil forces into Christian people? Even in the rare instances of people using incantations when the mixture is being shaken, this does not mean Christians should not use homoeopathic remedies any more than not using 'tainted money'.

Splitting the atom

We have already seen that homoeopathic remedies act as triggers in releasing energy which enables the body to speed restoration. We all know that as the atom has been split into smaller components it has released more energy. The same principle can be applied here. It was Einstein who declared, 'A small amount of water can release enormous energy.' Work by Dr Benveniste of France has shown that the process of shaking known as succussion transfers an imprint of the original substance onto the water/alcohol molecule, and it is this imprint which is carried through from one potency to the next one. Higher potencies have been found to be more effective than lower ones on occasions when they are indicated: more energy is released. Water can thus be charged with the electro-magnetic frequency of an allergen and used to relieve a patient's allergy symptoms. Meanwhile, the scientific investigation of homoeopathic remedies currently being undertaken in Australia by Dr Paul Callinan, and within Britain by Dr Cyril Smith, tend to suggest that during potentisation the remedy affects the crystal structure of water. There is, therefore, a scientific explanation for the action of the ultramolecular potencies. To attribute this to evil powers is only a superstitious idea, with no foundation in science or religion.

Predictable effects

The effect of each remedy is also predictable, and this suggests a physical effect rather than a spiritual one, so those who believe that someone prays over the pills to endow them with occult powers are clearly mistaken. The whole process of diluting the substances is a physical one, and one day it will no doubt be fully explained. Even if it is not, the therapy does not automatically become occult. Nor is there anywhere the least shred of evidence to suggest that frequent shaking and incantations carried out by individual people induce harmful results, either in homoeopathic pharmacies or among classical homoeopaths. If any of these practices has ever taken place, it can only have been in some weird splinter groups.

Encouraging signs

One encouragement is that the homoeopathic remedy is given to the patient in low concentration but high intrinsic energy state. It is this energy that is released to stimulate various bioenergetic systems in the body. It has also been suggested by some nuclear physicists that such imprinted energy patterns have self-replicating qualities. This would help to explain why the homoeopathic remedies work so well. These may actually 'reproduce' within the bioenergetic systems of the body, unlike orthodox drugs, which, as far as we know, are simply metabolised and afterward excreted.

In accepting homoeopathy we are following in the footsteps of many missionaries like Hudson Taylor who learned about the therapy along with others at the Missionary School of Medicine. Other missionaries today incorporate it into their medical training and fieldwork.

Practical discussion questions

1. Compare and contrast how someone with a quite severe allergic nasal reaction might be helped either by (a) orthodox medicine or (b) a regular visit to a homoeopath in his or her own locality.

2. Can you think of any examples in your own experience, or among your friends, of how the law of cure has been put into effect?

3. What reasons are there for rejecting the idea that preparing homoeopathic remedies enables Satan to gain a foothold in us?

4. Are there other ways in which homoeopathy can encourage us?

Question 24: Acceptable Practitioners
What Questions Do Christians Need to Ask Before Receiving Therapy?

We have seen that one of our main principles in PACT with regard to any therapy is, 'Whose hands is it in?' We may feel perfectly happy about a particular therapy but less happy about the person who is practising it in our locality. Alternatively we may feel happy about that person but feel the Lord is pointing out someone further afield as being the right practitioner for us to consult. In this chapter I would like to suggest three main questions that we may wish to ask before embarking on any course of treatment with a complementary therapist. Sometimes the answers will be obvious or easy to come by; in other cases we may have to ask around, read literature, or have an informal consultation with the practitioner first, before we are satisfied that we are taking the right course.

What does the treatment consist of, and what am I required to do?

It's important that we are each happy about the therapy that we are going to receive, about what sort of treatment we will be given, and about what response we are expected to make in order to benefit from it. If after receiving answers we are still unsure, we need to seek the Lord's guidance, get the help of trusted and experienced Christian friends, and possibly seek advice from our church leaders. We may also ask someone on the register of Christian therapists. We shall need to consider if the claims made for the therapy fit the facts. Take massage as an example. We know that massage can relax us and help us to feel better in ourselves, but the massage on offer may or may not be what we are looking for! Let's suppose we are offered rolfing. We may not know until we ask that this is a deep massage that breaks down connective tissues which should not be present.

Highly recommended

There are several different ways by which practitioners advertise for their clients. You may find them listed in *Yellow Pages*. They may have advertisements in the local press, or in natural health magazines. But the best means is probably through word of mouth, and when someone is 'highly recommended' to you by a relative or Christian friend you are less likely to be disappointed.

On one occasion a lay reader (a friend of ours) had a painful arm and we recommended an osteopath to her. Not only did she discover a tremendous difference in her arm but significantly the Lord provided exactly the right amount for the fee that she had to pay.

More confusion

But not everyone is so forthcoming. Someone from Harrogate wrote:

> 'Only a few weeks back a woman at church asked people to pray for a friend of hers with severe back pain – she wanted us to pray that God would protect her from "going down the path of alternative medicine." I felt like standing up and saying, "Don't be daft – if she's got back pain, osteopathy or acupuncture would be much more effective than anything her GP gives her!"

And there's also confusion sometimes about something like cranial-sacral therapy, because it includes the practitioner placing his or her hands on the sufferer's head, and because he or she sometimes appears to say or do little or nothing. In fact, the physiological system of the cerebro-spinal fluid's semi-hydraulic pumping action is being used to encourage the body to heal itself. This the therapist does by unravelling and balancing fascia and other soft tissues and even correcting the position of the cranial bones. This can be measured scientifically, but who has the facilities, time or money to embark on the project?

What are the therapist's credentials? To whom is she or he accountable?

Having satisfied ourselves about the treatment, we also need to be satisfied about the practitioner. In some cases we may have to find out as much as possible, but if we're consistent, remember that we should take the same approach with doctors and ministers!

Safe and competent

Osteopaths now have such rigorous training that we can guarantee that in the majority of cases they are safe and competent. If we are to discover whether other therapists are as well, we need to enquire about each one's background, training, qualifications, standards and accountability.

We are not always able to guarantee that everyone on the National Register of Christian Therapists is completely safe and competent – only that they are committed Christians. But obviously they are more likely to be, and you can, if you wish, check their background with the appropriate institutions listed in Appendix 3. A shiatsu therapist once wrote the following letter to us from Faversham, Kent:

> 'As a Christian involved in this field I have long felt too much fear and hysteria has surrounded this field of medicine. As more and more people are turning to complementary medicine for their health needs, I feel it vitally important that more Christians become therapists in order for the public to be in safe hands.'

Untapped potential

Yet that woman would agree with us that God uses non-Christians in this area as well, and with the notice that hung over the door of the famous psychologist Carl Jung's consulting room: 'Whether invoked or not, God will be present.' We would also agree with the chairman of the General Osteopathic Council, who has stated that there is vast untapped potential for health care in this country.

Incidentally, according to a survey publicised by the insurance company Legal and General, in the future the therapy people will be most likely to choose will be osteopathy. In addition, when those surveyed were asked which complementary therapy they would be most likely to choose,

- 51 per cent said osteopathy
- 35 per cent said homoeopathy
- 35 per cent said chiropractic
- 28 per cent acupuncture.

The survey also found that 36 per cent thought their GP would refer them to an osteopath.

A few of our contacts have both an orthodox and a complementary training. This gives us a bonus if we consult them, for such practitioners are blazing trails in the area of integrated medicine and therapy.

Are they accountable?

A servant should be willing to submit to others (Ephesians 6:5), and if practitioners are to serve us they should not be people who have set themselves up as isolated loners. Find out as well if the therapist you are considering using is subject to continuing professional development, which means he or she will be attempting to keep up with the latest information in his or her field.

A professional specialist

Because this is the sort of therapist we are looking for, remember that the therapies are only safe in the hands of experienced practitioners, and you, the reader, should never try any therapy on yourself, unless you have experience. The exceptions, of course, are using the 'first aid' remedies of homoeopathy and herbalism, and in the ministry of Christian healing, though it is not usually wise to lay hands on yourself as you are the one with the problem, and it has the effect of 'short-circuiting' the blessing. It is occasionally right, however, in a congregation where the leader encourages each person to do so. When once Smith Wigglesworth did this in Sweden, there were hundreds of people converted and healed as a result.

What is the therapist involved in? Does this affect treatment?

This is the additional dimension that Christians particularly are interested in. Without prying into the therapist's personal life we shall want to ensure that what he or she gives is pure homoeopathy, or pure reflexology – not with occult or astrological predictions. Even if we know that the practitioner is involved with things Christians question we may still be happy about receiving treatment as long as we receive the assurance that none of these form part of the treatment. Remember that techniques used by the enemy are not necessarily wrong either, and if you spot New Age books in the waiting room this again need not necessarily cause you to reject the treatment.

Dark areas

On the other hand, you may receive literature about aroma-therapy but then discover that the practitioner is a spiritualist. Noting the principle I have already outlined that the higher up the scale we go of body, soul and spirit, the more cautious we need to be, you would be unwise to have this individual give you hypnotherapy or spiritual healing. We have seen how it is by their fruits that we recognise people (Matthew 7:20), and this is the sort of way in which we can examine the fruits. (See Question 26 for a fuller investigation of the 'dark areas' that Christians should keep well away from except in missionary work.) Unorthodox aids to diagnosis, especially astrology, dowsing and divination, are among things we look out for (Deuteronomy 18:10). Remember that New Ager therapists are caring and will exhibit tenderness, but this should not blind us to what we believe is error in their practices. If after investigation you are still unsure about them, receive confirmation from other Christians or hold back from having a consultation until you are truly satisfied. But don't be afraid: there are plenty of acceptable practitioners.

Practical discussion questions

1. Choose one complementary therapy. Now list places where you can find general information about this subject, e.g. on the Internet.

2. Are you confused about any particular therapy or practitioner?

3. On entering a complementary medical practice you just have the sense that all is not well there. What steps might you take next?

4. How would you decide whom you'd approach for your own healing?

Question 25: **Spiritual Discernment**

In Complementary Medicine How Can I Avoid the Occult?

The other day I was driving the car in Tunbridge Wells town centre when all of a sudden a middle-aged woman stepped out in front of it. I did an emergency stop, but how I managed to avoid her I do not know. She had given no warning, and appeared to be unconcerned. It reminded me that, when there is no warning given, events could lead to catastrophe. That's why this section of the book is necessary.

I have already mentioned the unhealthy approach adopted by a number of Christians who want to associate everything in alternative medicine with the occult. But the other side of the coin is this, that many people involved with alternative medicine become mixed up in some way or another with things Christians should beware of. That is why our need of discernment is so great that, while we must be sure to keep the precious baby, we must learn to drain off the dirty bath water.

A vicar confessed, 'I find the whole area of alternative medicine such a minefield. When people ask me about it I never know what to reply.' Perhaps this chapter can help, as I explain more fully the three tools that can most enable us to discern what is right.

1. Scripture

In my answer to Question 12 I made it clear that Christians should not accept anything that goes against Scripture. If you believe it is the written word of God (2 Timothy 3:16), then a logical question to ask is, 'What does the Bible say about this sort of situation?' We must know and use it in deciding what is occult or questionable from a Christian point of view. Moreover, we should never go against the guidance in Scripture, so that if we receive guidance from another source and it contradicts the Bible, we must learn to reject it.

Let me list some of the Scripture references that can help us to see things more from God's point of view and so make decisions:

► **Deuteronomy 18:10–11**

> *'Let no-one be found among you who sacrifices his son or daughter in the fire, who practises divination or sorcery, interprets omens, engages in witchcraft, or casts spells, or who is a medium or spiritist or consults the dead.'*

(Note that some Christians foolishly use these verses to condemn complementary therapies, on the basis that what cannot yet be explained scientifically must be supernatural and therefore – in their estimation – must be evil.)

► **Matthew 7:20**

> *'... by their fruit you will recognise them.'*

Jesus is speaking of false prophets. 'Fruit' refers not just to results but to manner of life – compare Galatians 5:22–23: *'the fruit of the Spirit is love ...'*

► **John 14:6**

> *'I am the way and the truth and the life. No-one comes to the Father except through me.'*

New Agers tend to believe in relative rather than absolute truth. Sometimes their attitude is, 'Never mind if it's true in every sense as long as it works for you.'

► **1 Corinthians 6:19**

> *'Do you not know that your body is a temple of the Holy Spirit ...?'*

► **1 Corinthians 10:31**

> *'... whatever you do, do it all for the glory of God.'*

A good question to ask is, 'Will I by using this therapy/ practice be pleasing God?'

▶ **1 Corinthians 12:3**

> *'... no-one can say, "Jesus is Lord,"except by the Holy Spirit.'*

When it comes to *spiritual* approaches, any which do not acknowledge the Lordship of Christ have to be out of bounds for the believer, and we must trust Jesus to be the sole Initiator of mystical spiritual experiences.

▶ **Galatians 5:25**

> *'... keep in step with the Spirit.'*

Endeavour to be in the right place at the right time and to do what the Lord desires you to do.

▶ **1 Peter 3:15**

> *'Always be prepared to give an answer to everyone who asks you to give the reason for the hope that you have. But do this with gentleness and respect.'*

We represent Christ in such situations.

2. Sharing

While the Bible lays down general principles, it does not always give specific answers to the questions we are asking, and we may find some Christians interpreting the same verses in different ways. So we need to share with others. We saw in connection with Question 5 how this can help us overcome our fears, but it's also essential in assessing the whole area of alternative medicine and the dangers associated with it. And the same principle applies as in matters to do with healing: 'If you're not sure, share!' (2 Kings 20:8–11).

Where to share

Most of the time our sharing will be in private, or in our small groups, as we discuss the possibilities with those Christians who most understand us and are most on our spiritual wavelength. What do such people think about a particular situation? A decision may be reached after praying with them and listening for the answers. For *'All the believers were one in heart and mind'* (Acts 4:32).

Occasionally, however, the matters are resolved in public. If, for example, your church or group invites me to speak, I always give opportunity for questions, and sometimes there is a chance for a few people to share their own experiences. In cases where none of those present knows the answers we may be able to recommend specialists who can help.

Correcting abuse and misunderstanding

Sharing with other Christians may bring to light any particular problems among therapists which we had not realised were there. The occult practices a therapist is involved in may be revealed. One less overt thing to watch out for is abuse of power. Like the minister and the doctor, the therapist is in a position that commands respect but which also demands high ethical standards. Some abuses have been brought to light because Christians shared about them. We can act like salt in such situations (Matthew 5:13).

But sharing can also help to correct false interpretations of what is going on in the world of alternative medicine. One common misconception that Christians have helped to correct is that the five-pointed figure denoting the law of five elements, used on a daily basis by acupuncturists, is really the pentagram of witchcraft. The látter is immediately distinguishable, however, since it is upside down!

3. Spiritual gifts

The gift that, of course, is most needed in discerning the rights and wrongs of complementary medicine is again that of distinguishing spirits (1 Corinthians 12:10). This gift enables the Christian to know which kind of spirit is motivating a person at a particular time to speak or act: the Holy Spirit, the individual's human spirit, or an evil spirit. We must *'test the spirits to see whether they are from God'* (1 John 4:1), and then act accordingly: by supporting the therapist if God is using him or her, but, if not, by going elsewhere.

Satan's deceptions

But God and Satan are not like two equals in separate corners of a boxing ring. The devil has power but nothing like the power of Jesus who triumphed over all evil forces on the cross (Colossians 2:15). Yet he uses his strategies of temptation, oppression, depression, obsession and possession, working through doubt, deceit, division, disobedience and despair. He may have to use subtler wiles to deceive more experienced Christians, but every church needs at least one member who manifests the gift of discerning spirits. Leaders may be gifted in other ways but lacking in discernment.

Many people have been mobilised to speak and pray against occult activities but something more is needed. If the church made more use of the gift of distinguishing between spirits we might not see so many people turning to occult healers for reality, help and comfort. Nearly everybody requiring exorcism has been closely connected with the occult. They have been associated with one of three realms:

1. *the devilish* – areas such as satanism and black magic, where the devil is deliberately worshipped and obeyed (Revelation 12:9);
2. *the dangerous* – areas such as spiritism, white witchcraft, ouija, astrology and transcendental meditation, where people ostensibly receive help but in fact are being deceived by the enemy (1 Chronicles 10:13; Isaiah 8:19–20; 1 Timothy 4:1–2);
3. *the doubtful* – areas such as psychic healing and New Age therapies which are sometimes helpful, sometimes harmful, and about which we need discernment (1 John 4:1–3; Colossians 2:8).

Greater awareness

Professor Malcolm Stemp believes the main reason why the devil is interested in complementary medicine is that he wants to keep its benefits away from Christians! Thank God that when people are baptised in the Holy Spirit, they tend to have a greater awareness both of the supernatural and of the powers of evil. And the spiritual gifts that flow from this release of power can sharpen our awareness of each situation and show us what to do.

Ian Cowie, in *Across the Spectrum*, has this to say:

> 'When considering the rightness or the wrongness of any activity, we must not look at it in isolation, but consider its rightful place in a properly targeted life ... God is the ultimate mystery, and we must never think that we have God summed up and confined to any human words or institutions.' (p. 34)

In other words, don't limit Him!

Practical discussion questions

1. Have you had any dealings with the occult? What were the results?

2. *'Always be prepared to give an answer ... '* (1 Peter 3:15). If you are sure that a local therapy practice is not for the Christian, explain why.

3. Give examples of how, through sharing, you have discovered answers.

4. Is the gift of discerning spirits operating in your church? If not, how might it be recognised and introduced with your help?

Question 26: Harmful Experiences

What Sort of Practices Are Definitely Wrong for the Christian?

As this question is asked in the context of alternative medicine I shall confine my answer to arguments that are relevant to this area. I believe that God has at least ten 'commandments' to give us in this field, saying, 'Thou shalt not be involved in these practices.' Two of these areas we have explored in previous chapters: *Transcendental meditation* (Question 9) and *New Age experiences* of the harmful kind (Question 15). One important area I'll be covering at length in a later chapter is *spiritist phenomena* (see Question 29).

That leaves seven 'deadly sins' to be considered in this chapter. I believe that the Lord is grieved by all of these and SO IS SAD. In fact, the initials of each of these forbidden practices spell out these last three words:

- *Satanic rituals*
- *Occult activities*
- *Induced psychic experiences*
- *Sorcery and witchcraft*
- *Superstitious practices*
- *Astrological predictions*
- *Divination and dowsing*

As we look at each one we are not out to condemn people, many of whom are unwittingly drawn into these areas, but nevertheless we wish to expose the dangers involved, so that our readers will be more fully prepared if they come across them. And should an alternative therapist bring any of these into his or her treatment, we would advise the Christian client to consult another practitioner. As we have seen, there are plenty of therapists who have no such associations.

Satanic rituals

Satanist churches and black magic are not to be found in every street. Several cases in which people undergoing inner healing ministry were told they had been victims of satanic abuse were proved to be examples of 'false-memory syndrome'. However, satanism is rife in certain areas, and horrific practices such as making child victims pass through the fire and child sacrifice are not unknown. As today Christian rituals are rejected, so people are reverting to the very things from which our ancestors were glad to be delivered.

Some New Agers actually go in for Luciferic Initiation, and some rock music groups blatantly glorify Satan. However, most New Age people play this down. Under oriental influence they tend to deny the actual existence of evil, and in reaction against a fear-laden Christian fundamentalism they also play down sin. In various ways Satan thus turns people away from God and the truth (John 8:44).

Two types of group

The devil has two particular ways of deceiving us. The first is by causing some Christians to adopt such an over-the-top image of him that others dismiss it. For example, some extreme Christian groups become obsessed with exorcism, seeing demons in every illness and sowing a lot of fear in suggestible people. This is doing Satan's work for him, for people write them off as cranks, and Christianity with it.

The second way is to make people think there is no danger, and good intentions are enough. This is illustrated by the liberal group that reacts against teaching about Satan and ignores the reality of evil. It is making the dangerous mistake of underestimating the opposition. It is also operating in shady territory, even if it does not realise it. A watered-down gospel suits the devil very well.

'I'm a Satanist!'

All these things might suggest that Christians should avoid
Satanists. But if opportunity comes to us to get alongside them,
we need to remember that God loves these misguided individuals.
At a healing service at Doncaster, when a church secretary, Bert,
told us sadly, 'I've always wanted to witness to unbelievers about
Jesus', Chris and I promised to pray for him. The very next day he
was in the town's shopping centre, a very huge complex thronged
with Saturday shoppers. Wanting to sit down, he saw that the
seats provided were filled with people, but he managed to find one
space among them.

After a moment Bert was startled by the voice of a man sitting
next to him asking: 'You're a Christian, aren't you? I'm a Satanist!'
He was taken aback. He had never met the man before. But when
he had recovered his composure he spent over an hour talking
about Jesus and His atoning blood. He found the words just
flowed. God was answering our prayer for him more quickly than
he would have imagined! In the end he took the man for pie and
peas, a traditional northern dish.

2. Occult activities

The word 'occult', meaning 'hidden', has come to have a wider
meaning for Christians than it originally had. It tends to summarise all that is not of God in the areas of the mysterious and the
mystical. Occult knowledge becomes evil when it's kept hidden so
as to give the person who knows it power over others. It is
consequently sin.

In a number of New Age books it is claimed that Jesus gave
occult teaching that the disciples did not hand on in the Gospels
as we now have them. Against this we have His own sayings:

> *'There is nothing concealed* [occult] *that will not be disclosed ...
> what is whispered in your ear, proclaim from the roofs.'*
> (Matthew 10:26–27)

Occult books or charms

As we have seen, by involvement with the occult people can open
up themselves to evil forces. Those who possess occult books or
charms need to destroy them (Acts 19:19). A Christian called
Lilian was once given a Christmas present, which turned out to be
an idol. 'What should I do with it?' she asked. 'Destroy it!' Chris

and I replied. Although the person who gave it intended no harm, it had been dedicated to another god, so Satan could use it to bring Lilian into bondage. By destroying it she instead enjoyed peace.

We would recommend the same sort of drastic action with occult items such as ouija boards, which give guidance other than from God. And even when people have not played with ouija boards themselves but have been in the presence of others doing so, we reckon the best course is for those concerned to renounce and confess this. Like so many occult items the ouija board is a tool provided by Satan.

Other sects and cults

A number of pseudo-Christian sects and cults are actually occult. One of the problems of the last half-century has been an alarming number of people (especially young people) being drawn into these cults by charm and 'brainwashing'. The Moonies actually endorse a philosophy called 'Heavenly Deception', by which they will attempt to justify using all kinds of tricks to proselytise new converts.

And using 'occult' in the wider sense of the word, we should not be deceived by those sects which offer us healing using the names of God and Christ, such as Christian Science. To the adherent of this philosophy sickness and pain are not real. There is emphasis on Christ's teaching without His redemption, and the only 'key to understanding the Scriptures' is the writings of Mary Baker Eddy.

3. Induced psychic experiences

I mentioned these when considering energy. We saw that all psychic experiences are not necessarily wrong in themselves. Those such as intuition and premonitions may be God given. But others such as psychometry – holding an object owned by a person to receive his impressions or thoughts – are clearly wrong. And danger especially arises when people seek to induce, cultivate and develop psychic abilities. We would, therefore, warn against the practice of astral projection, seeking to enable oneself to come apart from one's body in order to do 'soul travel'. However, if such an experience just occurs without any inducement, this is not wrong for the Christian.

A number of people have had 'near-death experiences' during which, perhaps while undergoing operations, they hovered between life and death and looked down upon their bodies, sometimes experiencing bright lights and a number of unexpected occurrences. Demos Shakarian, founder of the Full Gospel Businessmen's Fellowship International, tells how God took him out of his body right round the world: first to see the faces of many men looking miserable and then to view the same faces looking happy and radiant.

The girl who turned back

One Sunday morning Vera, in her early twenties, appeared at our family service. 'I've heard you do healing,' she said. 'I've come because I suffer from epilepsy.' We discovered that she and her husband were involved in the occult and psychic experiences. She regularly talked with apparitions and he did automatic writing. We had a long discussion with them both, explaining what it would mean if Vera came to Jesus. 'He can set you free,' I said gently, 'but you must renounce these things and not dabble in them again.'

We took Vera to Trevor Dearing's church, where several demons were cast out of her (cf. Mark 9:25). We also sought to help her in our midweek group. But she still had fits and she appeared to make no progress spiritually. It was not long before we discovered why. Vera had not attempted to curtail her activities, in spite of our advice that she should. And as fast as the evil spirits left, she was as good as inviting them back (cf. Matthew 12:43–45).

4. Sorcery and witchcraft

I first heard Doreen Irvine give her testimony 'From Witchcraft to Christ' in 1972. She told how as Queen of the Witches she put curses on many people. She is one of many individuals who were so steeped in witchcraft that only intense deliverance ministry could bring her out of it – in her case from forty-eight demons (cf. Matthew 12:43–45).

Black and white witches

Witches are often 'ordinary people'. By day they work as doctors, teachers, lawyers, farmers, chefs, or in any other run-of-the-mill job. So they are not fun figures for Halloween, leftovers from a superstitious past, or poor innocent old women who were once persecuted during witch-hunts. In black witchcraft they call up the devil and enter into a relationship with him. Here I should in fairness again stress that this is not the dimension occupied by most New Age people. More of these are involved with white witchcraft, where they 'harness the forces of nature to bring about good'. But this, too, is out for the Christian, reflecting as it does a substitute for God in paganism, pantheism and nature worship.

'She's mine!'

Angela is a young lady who was sent by a witches' coven in Devon to pray against a Christian service in Tunbridge Wells, but the Lord spoke to her during the sermon and amazingly she was saved. She had, however, sold her soul to Satan, writing this in blood. So when we came against a demon in her it cried, 'She's mine!' – and it took six men to hold Angela down as her arms were filled with superhuman strength. But after she had undone her pact with Satan and put in writing that she had given her life to Christ, Angela was set free over a period from each of the demons that possessed her, one by one. She was eventually baptised, and was cared for by some students at a theological college. Like Simon the sorcerer of old she had discovered that Jesus had greater power (see Acts 8:13).

5. Superstitious practices

When St Paul commenced his first sermon at Athens he told his listeners, *'you are very religious'* (Acts 17:22). Interestingly, in the Authorised Version this is translated quite differently: *'Ye are too superstitious.'* But the one is not so distinct from the other, for what is superstition if not a religion, yet another body of belief which is a substitute for true faith and guidance? Superstition is basically faith in the wrong things and guidance from the wrong sources. It's quite different from the supernatural – although supernatural forces of evil use it for their own ends.

'I hope so'

Our nation is full of superstition and some of our churches are too! In parts of the world like Southern Ireland and Malta, for example, pictures of Mary are venerated in a superstitious manner. I appreciate that many people say 'Touch wood' or 'I'd better keep my fingers crossed' because it's really just another way of saying 'I hope so', and they have no deeper or evil intentions. But it's still a major barrier to some people putting their faith in the Lord, such as in show business where it's accepted as the norm, so it presents more of a problem than at first sight appears.

The danger arises when superstition is taken seriously, becoming not just a habit such as always carrying a rabbit's foot for luck but a way of life, so that a person is terrified of spilling salt or breaking a mirror. It becomes a substitute for faith in God when people put their trust in the St Christopher or the 'holy water', and a substitute for His guidance when they see a black cat and expect to have a lucky day. I always deliberately walk under a ladder just to show how ridiculous the whole thing is! As for venturing out on Friday the thirteenth, Isaiah 8:12 is clear as to what we all should do: *'do not fear what they fear'*. Colour and sound therapy can be useful if applied in the right way, but lucky colours and birthstones have no meaning for us.

6. Astrological predictions

Astrology is yet another substitute for faith and guidance. It may be that the stars have some influence upon the earth – just as the moon affects the tides. But in no way are we ruled and guided by the stars, as taught by this false science related to Zoroastrianism. There is also good reason to suggest that people born around the same time of year have similar characteristics, but this again has nothing to do with the stars. And what is most abhorrent to the Christian is the detailed prediction and fortune-telling involved.

Fortune-telling
This is very different from Christian prophecy. The guidance it offers is not only based on false premises but has nothing to say about the true goal of life, nor about moral values. For instance, if 'the stars say that Wednesday is a bad day for you to get far in your financial dealings', this could equally be true of the 'con man' and the collector for the Salvation Army. In fact, one man at our training days summed up such things as 'a real horror-scope'!

Alongside astrological predictions we must count many other forms of fortune-telling, such as palmistry, tarot, reading tea leaves, and a host of weird and wonderful attempts to predict the future. The question naturally arises, 'Are any of their predictions true?' And the answer is yes. In fact, sometimes gypsies have been spot-on in foretelling specific events that would occur in the lives of individual people. But this is another case of asking not only, 'Does it work?' but 'Is it right?' I believe the devil is behind all these false prophecies and once again, *'by their fruit you will recognise them'* (Matthew 7:20) for the counterfeits they are. The Christian has God's guidance and prophecies to go by instead.

7. Divination and dowsing

The last of these 'seven deadly sins' is another that is clearly condemned in the Bible (Deuteronomy 18:10). What is divination? The Hebrew word means 'throwing', referring to the old practice of throwing cards, arrows, dice, etc., to make up your mind what you should do. This practice depends on the belief that if you open the situation to 'chance', then the gods can guide you. This method of decision-making is forbidden. Whether or not you believe in chance or the gods, it is an immature way of making a decision!

But what about a football match? We toss up to decide which end we'll take. Is that breaking God's law? No, because the referee is not seeking the guidance of God or any outside intelligence. The 'supernatural element' is missing. It is not true divination.

What is forbidden is a coming-together of three elements: decision making, the element of chance, and seeking guidance elsewhere than from the living God. Therefore, it is not the physical action that is condemned but subjecting oneself to beings other than our God.

Casting lots

When after the death of Judas Iscariot the eleven apostles chose someone to replace him we read that *'they cast lots'* (Acts 1:26). Literally this can be translated, 'They divined'. But here the same principle applies. They were seeking guidance from God, so their divination was not wrong. So too other types of divination that do not involve 'throwing' – such as water-divining – are acceptable.

Pendulum swinging

We do, however, exclude dowsing or pendulum swinging. A Christian lady was very successful in treating people with diet and vitamin supplements but one of her clients wrote to me, concerned that she tended to use a pendulum to make a diagnosis. I wrote in reply:

'We have no doubt that pendulum swinging works and brings benefits, perhaps better than other forms of medicine. But these are not the main criteria by which a Christian decides whether or not something is right before God. We do not see it in the same sort of category as water-divining, as the answers received through the pendulum are thought to come from the client's subconscious mind, which is imperfect and part of our fallen human nature. While therefore the answers received will sometimes be correct, there's no guarantee that it's always what God wants, and there's a danger that the unprotected person may be opening himself up to Satan.'

Practical discussion questions

1. Jesus made a habit of loving the sinner and hating the sin. How can this be applied in our own lives to the experiences listed?

2. Do you know people involved in the occult? How would you seek to encourage them to give up these things and trust in the Lord?

3. What part does superstition play in the lives of your friends?

4. How would you encourage someone to stop reading his or her horoscope?

Question 27: Evil Spirits

*I Was Delivered from a Spirit of Reflexology –
Isn't It Wrong?*

No, reflexology is not wrong. As we have seen, it is one of many complementary therapies that are God-given and neutral aids to healing. Like orthodox medicine and many other practices it can be used for good or evil, but in itself it is not at all wrong.

Therefore, with respect, I question what has happened here. May I suggest the only possibilities that make any sense to me?

1. You're mistaken to think you were delivered from an evil spirit.

2. Yours was real deliverance, but not from a spirit of reflexology.

You see, the evil spirits only tend to attach themselves to sinful practices or to ones that are liable to lead people into sin. If an occult activity were involved, I could accept that you may have been delivered from a spirit of voodoo. If you were dabbling into questionable psychic experiences, I could believe you were perhaps delivered from a spirit of levitation. If you were deviating from God's will, I could understand your deliverance from a spirit of waywardness. But no way do I believe anyone has ever been delivered from a spirit of reflexology, or indeed acupuncture or homoeopathy.

Therefore, if you are absolutely sure that your deliverance was genuine – that an evil spirit did actually leave you when ordered to in the name of Jesus – this must have been a spirit of another kind. If you shared with the people ministering to you that you had been to a reflexologist, and if they had a false understanding of reflexology, this may be why they decided it was a spirit of reflexology. But it may be that the reflexologist was involved in occult activities, and it is *these* that caused you to be demonised – particularly if you co-operated by involvement in them yourself.

Experiencing evil spirits

Having answered your question, let me use the rest of this chapter to answer some of the many questions asked me about evil spirits. One evening at Hildenborough the last person who came forward to me for ministry was a young lady who asked me to pray about her catarrh. Hardly had I begun when she was taken over by an evil spirit of fear, which had manifested itself in reaction to God's power. I cast out the demon and the girl felt better. This incident reminds us that it's impossible for any of us to minister healing for long before we shall find ourselves dealing with evil spirits.

Mental illness?

Now, I am well aware that some of the cases which people regarded in Bible times as sickness caused by evil spirits are what today we would call mental illness. But there are many instances in the Scriptures where this is not the case, and in particular we find that while mental illness is usually gradually healed, deliverance from demons is swift. It's logical also, if Christians believe in a spiritual realm, that they should not expect illnesses just to be of the body or the mind. If you are still not convinced about demons, just attend an exorcism and try to explain it otherwise!

Of course, there are similarities with mental problems. Those who hear voices in their head may be schizophrenic, may have become demonised, or may be Christians listening to the Lord! That's why once again discernment is so necessary. We were once invited to minister to a clergyman's daughter in Tonbridge for mental problems. Elizabeth spoke intelligently to us most of the time, but every so often she started swearing and cursing our children. We might easily have concluded that she was demon possessed, but we decided that it was all due to the mental problems she had experienced following a difficult birth. And we were encouraged to know that other experienced people who ministered to her felt the same. Here let me add that, even when we are dealing with people who have been fully demonised, they are seldom evil people. Rather they have been invaded in the same way as germs invade our bodies.

Fallen angels

At one of our training days a questioner was exercised by tension between our talk of rebuking demons and Jude 9 where only God may rebuke Satan. But that context is not one of healing, and we seldom have to deal with Satan directly. More often it's his agents, the fallen angels he uses to turn people from God (Revelation 12:7). Several types of evil spirit are mentioned in the Bible besides the spirits of infirmity I referred to when answering Question 3. There are spirits of divination or fortune-telling (Acts 16:16), familiar spirits – referring to ones running within a family (1 Samuel 28:3 AV), and unclean spirits (Mark 1:27, AV). The latter are often taken to refer to demons connected with sexual sins, but it can be a general term for various demons.

Susceptible people

We should be careful to remember that all people dabbling in the occult do not automatically become demonised. Just as some people are susceptible to heart attacks, others to strokes and others to breakdowns, so some people are more susceptible to the holds that Satan can gain over them than others. Nevertheless, to ensure complete protection we advise no involvement in this 'dark area'.

Exposing evil spirits

Satan's tactics

Evil spirits can sometimes take us all off guard, because they can be very well organised. One of Satan's favourite tactics is to blow up little things to make them appear large. Another is to pretend to hide away in the hope that he and his agents will be ignored. In cases of multiple possession the last demon, which is usually also the strongest, sometimes succeeds in convincing those ministering that it is non-existent. Another tactic is to twist what is said so that someone hears something different from what was spoken. And a favourite approach is to wear down people – especially during long exorcism sessions – by delaying tactics.

An apocryphal story is told of a meeting with the devil and his agents in which Satan called for ideas as to how to turn people away from God. One evil spirit suggested, 'I'd tell them there is no God.' 'That's no good,' answered Satan, 'many of them are too intelligent to think the world's all an accident.' A second demon proposed, 'I'd tell them there is no hell.' 'That's no good either,' replied Satan, 'many have already experienced hell on earth.' Then a third spirit piped up, 'I'd tell them there is no hurry.' 'Ah!' exclaimed the devil, 'now that's the best idea I've ever heard!'

Satanic oppression

The closer we grow to the Lord, the more the devil is likely to assault us. A Kent doctor wished to use Christian healing with his patients as well as medical treatment, and when I ministered to him, the Lord said he was anointing his hands for the task. But when I prayed with the doctor's wife I viewed a picture of grass growing but, as fast as it started to grow, it was mown down again. The devil was cutting short her growth in the Lord, and I prayed God would restore and maintain in her what she had been robbed of.

In our contemporary situation Satan often directs his evil spirits to pressurise God's children by splitting families, discouraging them, pressurising them, robbing them of time, draining their finances, plaguing them with uncertainties and playing on their weaknesses. Sometimes this oppression can literally be felt, as, for example, in the case of a church which said its prayers 'were not reaching the ceiling'.

How to discern

Even when we are not given the gift of discerning spirits we can detect when evil spirits are at work. One way is, as we have seen, by discovering the origin of a person's problems; another is by the symptoms manifested. We can discern much through external manifestations, physical sensations and inward revelations. Unusual voices, eyes, smells, moans, strength, etc., can indicate a heavy presence of evil, along with a cold atmosphere, animal behaviour, an inability to move and a disturbing situation. Some

Christians find their hair stands on end or their faces harden in reaction to such evil manifestations. I may experience icy feet; Chris may be hit by a sense of blackness. She also experiences a 'spirit of heaviness' (Isaiah 61:3) or a 'spirit of enthusiasm', according to the nature of what is happening.

Encountering evil spirits

Resisting

We shall look at deliverance ministry in connection with Question 30. Here notice that there is much that we can all do to counteract evil spirits. We can all put on the whole armour of God (Ephesians 6:10–18). And James' advice is: *'Resist the devil, and he will flee from you'* (James 4:7). When Jesus was tempted He resisted the devil using the sword of the Spirit, the word of God (Ephesians 6:17). Each time He was attacked He answered, *'It is written . . . '* (Luke 4:4, 8, 10).

Rebuking

There are times, however, when we are not only to defend ourselves but also attack the enemy, and the simplest form of attack is rebuking. Jesus rebuked demons (Matthew 17:18), sicknesses (Luke 4:39) and other forms of evil (Mark 4:39). We can come against them in His name and use the authority He has given us over evil (Matthew 10:1).

A lady called Glenys had a husband who would constantly beat and ill-treat her. But she began to see his acts as motivated by the devil through an evil spirit. So each time that he went for her, she would cry out, 'I rebuke you, evil spirit, in the name of Jesus!' Instantly, on each occasion, the man either turned deathly pale or was thrown back across the room by the mighty power of the Lord.

A minister at Plymouth once refused to give anything to a tramp who called on him, and in consequence the tramp brandished a knife. But the minister commanded, 'I bind you, evil spirit, in the name of Jesus!' Immediately the tramp's raised arm became immovable. Glancing at a picture of Jesus on the wall, the tramp surprisingly exclaimed, 'Would you mind asking that bloke to let go of my arm?' He automatically knew whom he was up against!

Our battleship

John Wimber pointed out that people go to church so often to be bolstered up instead of to take part in a battle with the devil. But he stressed that the church is not like a luxury liner but more like a fully equipped battleship. It is in conjunction with our Christian brothers and sisters, therefore, that we can make the most impact on the enemy. God has put all things under Jesus' feet (Ephesians 1:22), and we are seated with Him in heavenly places (whether we feel like it or not – Ephesians 2:6). Therefore, our enemies are under *our* feet too, and as Charles Wesley reminds us in *Soldiers of Christ, Arise*, we in the church can 'tread all the powers of darkness down'.

Two things in particular appear to frighten evil spirits. One is Spirit-filled worship: as we sing in *Onward, Christian Soldiers*, 'Hell's foundations quiver at the shout of praise'. The other is water. That is why baptism can be such a powerful opportunity to declare, 'I renounce evil'. In some cases where people with satanic tattoos have been baptised, the tattoos have disappeared by the time they have come out of the water!

When we ministered at Crawley, my wife saw a picture of some mice pegging garments on a clothes-line. The Lord was saying that evil forces had specific holds on one woman through guilt, hurt and fear. Our task was to remove these pegs through the ministry. Jesus can use you in similar ways to claim the victory for Him.

Practical discussion questions

1. Which types of evil spirit might Christians encounter today?
2. How would you distinguish whether someone was mentally ill or demonised?
3. 'I'd tell them there is no hurry.' Can you think of examples in your situation of how events have been delayed by the enemy?
4. Which sections of the armour of God have you found most useful?

Discernment

Question 28: 'Losing' Healing
I'm Healed But My Sickness Returns – Is This the Devil?

I do not like the phrase 'losing healing', because it can suggest again that healing is a commodity that has been obtained rather than a development of the work that God is doing in the person. However, I appreciate that when people use this phrase they are referring to the experience they have had of apparently being healed through prayer and then something has come along – perhaps soon afterwards – to knock this idea on the head. I sympathise with such people, as I have had the same experience on occasions. I have learned, however, not to think it is always the devil who has spoilt their progress. There are, in fact, four main possibilities that may have occurred.

1. You were not really healed at all, though it appeared you were

Some conditions, such as leukaemia, can go into quite substantial periods of remission. You may have clearly experienced a temporary alleviation of your symptoms but not been completely cured. There are those Christian leaders, as we have seen, who insist that if you claim your healing by faith you are healed, even if you are still hobbling around. If this was your experience, you should not be surprised to find that they were wrong, and that more is required.

Taking your temperature

Now just as we tend to take our temperature most when we are ill, so this is a very good time to assess your progress in the Lord. Of course, only He knows the full extent of this, but you can gain a good idea, and with prayer and perhaps sharing with others you will no doubt be able to ascertain more about your own situation. There is truly no need for you to have a sense of failure, whatever the cause of your problem.

Worse before better

In complementary medicine things often have to get worse before they get better. Chris has to warn people that they may be very stiff and sore the day after she has treated them, but after that the body tends to adjust to the new situation. In the church, too, sometimes events work out in this manner. An itinerant healing minister was taken ill and after prayer grew progressively worse but then made a remarkable recovery. A lay reader we ministered to for arthritis was much worse three days afterwards but after another three days was fine. It may sometimes take time for bad things to come to the surface and leave us. In physical healing, dormant and unused muscles may have to adjust. In inner healing a deeper layer of need may be surfacing and require dealing with.

2. You were healed of symptoms, but the root cause has not been hit

The answer to Question 17 revealed how it is so often necessary to discover the root cause(s) of an ongoing problem before there is a complete cure.

'Get to the source'

On one occasion, while a Breath member was ministering to a woman of eighty-six, the Lord said, 'Get to the source.' The woman had back trouble and one leg proved to be shorter than the other. As Jean held her foot and prayed, the smaller leg shot out to the same length as the other. Jean couldn't stop laughing at the suddenness of what the Lord had done! Find the vital spot and things happen!

Identifying with others?

A man at another training day remarked, 'I have been told that I can identify better with other people who have my illness if I remain unhealed. I don't think that's so, but what do *you* think?'

I replied as follows: 'You are in a good position to identify with others with the same affliction, but you'll be in an even better position if you're healed. The Bible tells sick Christians to seek healing (James 5:14–16), so to stay as you are would be neglecting

God's word, even though He can use you while you're still weak and unwell. If people tell you to remain unhealed they are not showing the love Jesus had for the sick. Even many unbelievers would want you well, so anyone who really cares about you will feel the same. If you share about your experiences with others suffering from the same affliction, they will appreciate what you have suffered and they should recognise that you understand their feelings too.'

3. You were fully healed, but Satan is counterfeiting your symptoms

In connection with Question 3 I drew attention to the fact that spirits of infirmity (Luke 13:11) have the task of causing people to be sick. Here I'm suggesting that when someone has been healed, these spirits can also make it look as though this is not so by recreating the symptoms that the person used to have. In fact, we have noted three main tasks of spirits of infirmity:

1. *causing sickness* – which needs discernment to be ascertained
2. *'curing' sickness* – by different kinds of counterfeit healing
3. *counterfeiting sickness* – notably after healing through prayer.

Again discernment is required to recognise this, but, once we do, it is a comparatively straightforward problem to deal with. In fact, we simply need to say, 'Away from me, Satan!' as Jesus did (Matthew 4:10).

The old landlord

The devil is actually the old landlord of our lives. When he still comes round demanding rent we don't argue with him but tell him, 'Take it up with the new landlord' (Jesus). This is in effect what happened with Sue, a Breath member who suffered from an umbilical hernia. At a meeting at Hildenborough she was over-joyed, as when we laid hands on her the power of God flooded through her and she felt a complete release in her body. But the next day Sue's pains were worse than they had ever been. Then a Christian friend called and discerned that Satan had been counterfeiting Sue's symptoms. Together they rebuked him in this situation, and immediately Sue felt another release.

We must be careful to be sure this *is* the cause. One man in bed felt things happening and kept rebuking Satan, but in fact it was the Lord continuing in him the work He had started earlier that day!

Side-effects of healing

Notice, too, that another aspect of the enemy's work is to cause the healing to seem to have side-effects. One side-effect of a drug may be drowsiness: similarly Satan may cause the healed person to become spiritually lazy. Then another is nausea: Satan may worry the healed person with feelings of sickness. And another is blurred vision: Satan may cloud the person's outlook with constant bouts of doubt and discouragement.

4. You were healed, but circumstances have restored your problems

If the healed person goes back into sins or circumstances which first brought on his or her problems, then the sickness is liable to reoccur. We have seen that unless those circumstances are changed or unless the person is able to get out of them, the same physical problems may keep coming back. It is common know-ledge that those who suffer a heart attack must take up a different lifestyle, paying special attention to diet and exercise. And we all need to watch our 'weak spots' to ensure we don't bring back our former problems.

How sin prevents healing

Those Christians are wrong who always say to people, 'If you are sick you must have sinned in a particular way.' However, there are times when it is sin that prevents healing or prevents it being maintained. In John 5:14 Jesus said to the healed man at the Pool of Bethesda, *'Stop sinning or something worse may happen to you.'* Whether his sin was resentment at seeing others being able to get into the pool before him, we do not know. But we do know sin can spoil healing. When people are in pain, that is not the best time to inform them that their sickness is due to some sin. What they need at that point is the loving word and gentle touch that can ease the pain in the name of Jesus. But we must not dodge the sin problem, and there is always going to be a right time to bring things out into the open.

Throughout the Bible we see how sin gets in the way of healing. Why is it that Elisha could raise a dead boy but his old servant Gehazi could not (2 Kings 4:31–35)? One reason was because the servant was deceitful (2 Kings 5:20–22). His heart wasn't right before God and he needed to repent. In fact, because of his sin Gehazi ended by being afflicted with the very disease of which Naaman had been healed: when he left Elisha's service, *'he was leprous, as white as snow'* (2 Kings 5:27).

It is not usually necessary to have to go looking for things to repent of if this is our experience. We shall either already know our weaknesses, or God will bring them to light during ministry.

A poignant example

Bishop David Pytches tells the case of one married couple who received ministry in the Vineyard Fellowship in Orange County, California. The wife was a physician and was healed of a physical ailment. The husband was filled with the Holy Spirit at the same meeting. When they all went home everybody was remarking on the wonderful change in her husband, and the wife began to feel so jealous of him that her healing left her. She phoned her pastor in great anguish. He discerned the root of the problem and told her to repent of this jealousy, which she did. Her healing returned immediately, thus making it absolutely clear what had happened.

Practical discussion questions

1. Have you ever enjoyed healing and then 'lost' it? Why was this?

2. A blind friend of yours attends a blind club held on church premises. He insists that he's fine. What can you do to help him?

3. Someone in your church was involved in the occult but received deliverance. Now her problems have returned. What do you advise?

4. How would you encourage those who have been recently healed to keep that way?

Question 29: Spiritist Healing

What Can I Say to a Sick Person Who Intends Using Spiritualism?

We come here to the last of the 'ten commandments' which I believe God desires us to obey in relation to practices which grieve Him, and which if used in treatment by an alternative therapist should cause Christians to refuse that treatment. A spiritist is someone who claims to communicate with the dead, and by a spiritualist we mean someone who regards this practice as a fundamental part of his or her religion. It is not always immediately obvious who is a spiritist healer. Sometimes such practitioners may also call themselves 'spiritual healer', 'spiritualist healer', 'psychic healer', or simply 'healer'. So it is always important to enquire what the healer does.

Its condemnation in the Bible

The first thing to point out to the sick person intending to use spiritism is that it is roundly condemned in the Bible. This fact may mean nothing to the non-Christian person but can be a means of helping to persuade anyone who takes the Scriptures seriously.

What God detests

We have already noticed how Deuteronomy 18:10 forbids anyone from being *'a medium or spiritist or* [one] *who consults the dead'* and clearly states that *'Anyone who does these things is detestable to the Lord'* (Deuteronomy 18:12). Saul died because he *'even consulted a medium for guidance'* (1 Chronicles 10:13). In Isaiah 8:19 we also read:

> *'When men tell you to consult mediums and spiritists, who whisper and mutter, should not a people enquire of their God?'*

It is clear that the Lord detests spirit guides, séances, the activities of mediums, and trances which are induced.

'Christian spiritualists' attempt to justify these practices by referring to Christ, but their hymns tend to obscure the gospel by changing references to Jesus' blood into mention of His love.

Communicating with the dead

When we come to the New Testament there are no direct references condemning spiritism, but the fact that there is not one single reference to people seeking to communicate with the dead should be sufficient to warn us that this is not part of the Christian gospel! Two particular passages are especially said by spiritists, however, to give support to their activities. One is where, during His transfiguration, Jesus converses with both Moses and

Elijah (Matthew 17:1–8). But He does not have to 'call them up', and their conversation is not about 'the other side' but about His death which was soon to take place (Luke 9:31). The other reference is to the *'great cloud of witnesses'* with which we are surrounded (Hebrews 12:1). This refers to the Old Testament saints that the writer has just listed. But even if these are watching us now – in which case they can see our sufferings and pain – there is no exhortation to contact them or have any communication with them.

Channelling
When Christians speak about being a 'channel', they are often referring to being a channel of God's healing. However, in New Age channelling the mediums see themselves as each guided by some 'higher spirit', such as that of a Chinese doctor who lived thousands of years ago. One translation of 'medium' is, in fact, 'he who has a knowing one', and this aptly describes the spirits that New Age people are speaking about. Other New Agers refer to themselves as 'sensitives'. These are not claiming to be mediums passing on some information from the dead but psychic channels able to pass messages from one level to another. Occasionally therapists have suggested doing channelling to help their clients. We advise Christian people to refuse such offers, and to claim the protection of Jesus' blood (cf. Exodus 12:13).

Notice, too, that many Christians feel that trying to communicate with departed saints is also wrong – in fact we've no guarantee they can hear us – and that we should not pray to angels: it is up to God if He wishes to communicate with us through them (Hebrews 1:14).

Why they consult spirit guides
The Bible says,

> *'For there is one God and one mediator between God and men, the man Christ Jesus ... '*   (1 Timothy 2:5)

But spiritualists who claim to be Christians say Jesus is both a mediator *and* a medium. They attempt to justify consulting spirit guides by drawing parallels like these: 'We do not go to the Queen every week for our pensions, we expect to get them from one of her lower officials. If we go to a bank, we do not expect to see the manager every time, but we do our normal transactions with the person behind the counter. In the same way we deal normally with our spirit guides, not God.'

This line of reasoning might ring true if the New Testament didn't make absolutely clear that we can come directly to God through Christ (John 14:6; Ephesians 2:18, etc.). We have no need to go through intermediaries, even if these were genuine. We can *'approach the throne of grace with confidence'* (Hebrews 4:16) and not be side-tracked.

It is a counterfeit type of healing

Not all spiritist healing will be counterfeit. Some may be genuine natural healing. Nevertheless, spiritist healing is to be avoided because we believe so much of it is of the enemy. Many Christians are convinced that the messages mediums receive are not from the spirits of the dead but from evil spirits impersonating them. Even if they *were* genuinely from the dead, the messages are frequently banal, and very little knowledge coming through tends to be truly enlightening – the spirits appear to be no better or wiser than us.

The world of spirits
This is not to say that Christians do not believe there are such beings as spirits – in fact *'God is spirit'* (John 4:24) – but we do not believe departed spirits can normally communicate with us. In our view, so-called ghosts may be explained in terms of place memories, energy, poltergeists or evil spirits, and contacting them is wrong. Ian Cowie in *Across The Spectrum* reaches this conclusion:

> 'When, instead of growing in the Spirit, people try to take short cuts to the spiritual through the medium of someone else's psychic gifts, something has gone wrong.'   (p. 97)

Something better
All these things can be communicated to the sick person who is considering trying spiritualism, and the best way to explain it is probably by declaring that Christians have something better.

However, it is only the Holy Spirit who can open people's eyes to see the difference. For over ten years I used to lead a monthly Praise, Healing and Renewal service at Shoeburyness, Essex. Brian was a young man who appeared at this one evening, and afterwards, responding to my invitation to people wanting to know more, he stopped and spoke with several of us. When we asked him if he went to church, he said, 'Yes, the Spiritualist church.' We gently tried to find out where he stood and it transpired that he was thrilled with our service but still wished to attend his own church where healing also took place. He could see no difference between the two.

For several months Brian attended and enjoyed our healing service but still could see no reason for leaving the Spiritualist church. Then one day he listened to the testimony of a friend of ours who used to be a spiritist. Suddenly everything clicked into place, and all desire for spiritism left him. He renounced his involvement.

Chris once read a book that told how, when a medium was taken over by 'the spirit of an ancient doctor', the medium's face was transformed into the face of the doctor. But why should the devil have all the best transformations? Some years later Chris and I were ministering to a handicapped girl when all of a sudden the lady with us saw Chris's face undergo a remarkable transformation and become the face of Jesus. Yes, we've something better to offer!

Its consequences to the person

The other main point to convey to the sick person considering the use of spiritism is that, even when there is remarkable physical cure as a result of spiritist healing, the person concerned often ends up in a worse state emotionally and spiritually. We in Breath have had to minister to hundreds of such people, and they often require deliverance ministry or exorcism before they are set free. We have also noticed that such people sometimes cannot stand the power-ful atmosphere of our healing meeting and have to leave it.

The presence of evil

Sometimes the people requiring help are the people we would least expect. One morning when I was a vicar at Huddersfield we were due to minister to Sally. She was a former student at Bible college, now married with two children. Her problems lay in her past and she had asked for inner healing. But as the ministry progressed the room grew icy cold and we were very aware of the presence of evil.

We had noticed on other occasions that demons only tend to manifest themselves among Christians when the power of the Lord is fully released, just as they cried out in the real presence of Jesus when He walked the earth – though they didn't automatically flee at His presence, but had to be told to go (e.g. Luke 4:33–35).

As we continued to pray and praise, Sally quite suddenly leapt out of her chair and started slithering around on the floor like a snake, her face contorted. She came leering at us with loud hissing noises. We came against the evil forces with the authority of Christ. The hissing immediately stopped and Sally's appearance changed to that of a serpent trying to charm. She half rose from her horizontal position and stretched out vertically. Her arms were high in the air, her body twisting and turning, and her face took on an alluring, bewitching expression. During the battle that followed she alternated between these two manifestations, and when the spirit left her she dropped to the floor like a stone and lay as though dead. After a while she opened her eyes and spoke to us: 'Someone at Bible School discerned that I had evil spirits. I was ministered to there but thought I was cleared. You see, when I was about ten I met spiritists and started to train to be a medium.'

'Well, let's praise the Lord for what He's done,' I suggested. But no sooner had we started to sing than Sally was taken over again. This time her face was changed into that of a pig. We urged her to co-operate with us when she was able and together we wrestled against principalities and powers. 'I know how that one got there,' she said afterwards. 'We used to call on the spirit of the pig. Thank God, He has set me free!' We were all exhausted, but elated.

Practical discussion questions

1. You pray for a woman and she is not physically healed. She then goes to a spiritualist and is healed. What might you do next?

2. What hope does the Bible bring that is different from spiritism?

3. How would you explain that spiritist healing may be counterfeit?

4. How can testimonies help convince spiritists about the gospel?

Question 30: Deliverance Ministry
Can Deliverance Be Done at a Distance?

Professor C.H. Joad, who took part frequently in the radio programme *The Brains Trust* many years ago, used to have a favourite saying: 'It all depends what you mean.' And that's my brief answer to this question. If by 'deliverance' the questioner means exorcism, then it would be unwise, for instance, to attempt this over the phone, for you cannot easily tell the state of the person or how far he or she is responding. If by 'deliverance' is meant setting the person free from a habit or difficulty, this is occasionally possible at a distance, but generally deliverance ministry is best in the presence of the person concerned – and where exorcism takes place it is usually wisest for more than one Christian to be ministering.

Sometimes the example of the Syro-Phoenician woman's daughter is offered as an instance of where Jesus did deliverance from afar (Mark 7:24–30). But this is not a normal instance of deliverance, for Jesus did not cast out the evil spirit but rather uttered a message of knowledge: *'the demon has left your daughter'* (v. 29).

The best approach

It is clear that different types of ministry will be required for different types of problem and the extent of the problem will determine the remedy we apply – such as peace, touch, drugs, psychiatry, inner healing, deliverance or exorcism – but nearly always the best approach is in treating someone in his or her presence.

In this chapter we are going to explore the four main types of deliverance ministry. As we do, notice that all deliverance must be in the powerful name of Jesus, which gives us our authority, and on the basis that He has won the victory over all evil powers.

Letting go

This is the simplest form of deliverance, one that is possible for any believer. Some difficulties are too big to be overcome through our own prayers, but others can be overcome as we simply claim the victory Jesus has won for us (1 Corinthians 15:57) and in His name resist the devil, recognising that he is the source of the fear, the misunderstanding, or whatever the problem may be. We should not be surprised at what God can accomplish through us!

However, when Jesus said believers would be safe if they picked up snakes (Mark 16:18) He didn't mean (as some sects in America believe) that Christians will be safe if they deliberately do this. That's like saying I'll be protected if I deliberately walk under a bus. But if we are walking in the Lord's will and clothed in His armour (Ephesians 6:11) we shall be safe even if all that we can do at that point is to stand firm and hold tight (Ephesians 6:14)!

Binding evil powers

Jesus has also given authority to us to restrict all evil powers. He promised, *'Whatever you bind on earth will be bound in heaven'* (Matthew 18:18). When we address evil forces and say, 'We bind you in the name of Jesus', this has the effect of leaving them bound and gagged, so unable to harm anyone present, just as when God shut the mouths of the lions that would otherwise have devoured Daniel (Daniel 6:22).

When a believer is led to cast out an evil spirit from a person or place, the demon usually needs to be specifically addressed and bound before it is commanded to go (Matthew 12:29). This is one reason why inexperienced, untrained or fearful Christians should not take the lead in exorcism ministry, though all believers can at some point be involved in some way in deliverance (Mark 16:17).

Setting free

Jesus also gave believers the authority to release people from evil and harmful things. He promised, *'Whatever you loose on earth will be loosed in heaven'* (Matthew 18:18). This is the most common form of deliverance, and something else which any Christian has authority to do under the Holy Spirit's leading. However, as some problems sometimes prove to be more complicated than envisaged, it's again usually best for inexperienced Christians to let people take the lead who have dealt with these sorts of problems before.

Cutting through chains

We have seen that when a problem is small it may be overcome by our own personal prayers, as it's like a piece of string which can easily be snapped. But when a problem is like a big chain around us we may need someone else to use the appropriate key to unlock the chain in the name of Jesus. As the sword of the Spirit can cut through chains, Christians can speak God's word to people who are bound to harmful things and say, 'We cut you free in the name of Jesus.' As one woman was set free in this way from bondage to her mother, her sister, who was miles away, simultaneously shook from head to foot. The same sort of powerful effects have resulted when curses put on individuals by satanists or black witches have been broken by the authority of Christ. The results can be instant and dynamic.

Here I would point out that when Paul writes of *'the sword of the Spirit, which is the word of God'* (Ephesians 6:17), while it can include the Bible, he was probably thinking mainly of the spoken word, which is the main tool we use in all forms of deliverance.

Apart from evil spirits there are four principal areas in which people need deliverance in the sense of being set free from what harms:

1. Ancestral ties
Both sins and sicknesses may 'run in the family' (Exodus 20:5), so one thing we can do is thank God for everything good someone has inherited but ask the Lord to set individuals free from bondage to their parents and ancestors, so that harmful things inherited will be cut off at the root. In this healing of the family tree it is both wrong and unnecessary to minister to the dead. The ministry is perfectly effective if given to the living person at his or her end of the chain. It can also clear the way for other healing to take place.

2. Authority figures
Some people are psychologically bound in a harmful way to people in authority who have dominated them or caused them to fear, such as their parents, teachers, doctors, police and pastors. We can cut them free in the name of Jesus, but such a deliverance may have to be reinforced several times before the person recognises the full benefit in relation to the one who has dominated him or her. Notice that when Jesus raised Lazarus from the dead, he was at first still bound and gagged (John 11:44). This can be the state spiritually of even Spirit-filled Christians until we set them free. They may also be bound by traditions and inhibitions.

3. Addictions and habits
Jesus further sets people free through deliverance ministry from all kinds of habits and addictions: to drugs, sexual perversions, violence, gambling, drinking, smoking and compulsive behaviour.

4. Attitudes and inabilities
We deliver the person from a negative attitude and minister the opposite to this: love for fear, forgiveness for resentment, peace for anxiety, assurance for guilt, healing of memories for hurt. We also minister new abilities: to relax, be flexible, decisive, etc.

Sending off

Sending evil spirits from places they are haunting or oppressing is something else in which only experienced people should take the lead. Donald Omand has ministered in this way on the roads at several accident black spots.

'Haunted houses'

Our own experience has been in cleansing the occasional 'haunted house'. We were called to a house in Oxfordshire to which a Christian couple wanted to move. But several people had been put off from buying the house because of 'the strange goings-on there' since it was occupied previously by a beauty queen and her partner. When we entered the house we were hit by a sense of evil, and this much intensified in one room where Buddha had been worshipped and sacrificed to. But by the time we were cleansing the kitchen we felt a lightness of spirit. The couple were shortly afterwards able to move into the house. They have lived there several years without experiencing any problems.

Casting out

Believers who cast out demons find it an exhilarating but costly experience. Sometimes it means spending several days in prayer and fasting (Mark 9:29, AV), and Satan's agents get to know those they are dealing with face to face (Acts 19:15).

Christians needing deliverance

We may need to discern in which areas Satan has a hold on someone and consequently how to minister. Some Christians who were demon-possessed before they were saved may need deliverance afterwards. When people are born again, their sins are forgiven but they can still fail; they are healed but they can still fall sick; and they have left the kingdom of Satan for the kingdom of God but, if the enemy still has a hold on them, he will not always let go until specifically commanded to. I have met many Christians who needed deliverance.

There's no point in looking for evil spirits, and there's no need to fear them if we walk with the Lord. But, should we Christians discern their presence, we have Jesus' own authority to deal with these demons (Matthew 10:1; Mark 16:17). Although Simon the sorcerer believed and was also baptised (Acts 8:13), Peter discerned that he was still *'full of bitterness and captive to sin'* (Acts 8:23). And although new Christians may have renounced evil and occult involvement, Satan may still have a hold on them in a related area that they have forgotten about, so deliverance may be necessary.

Challenging the demons

In cases of multiple possession we get to know when we are dealing with some demons that are stronger than others. Quite often there are two 'bodyguards', perhaps mocking spirits that cause the person to giggle or jeer when taken over. Then may follow the stronger demon that has often come in through connection with the occult. The bodyguards must be removed in advance of the stronger force.

Casting out demons involves directly challenging them. Some people prefer not to lay hands on a person while he or she is taken over by the powers of darkness and, therefore, while the touch is ministered for healing, it is usually the word for deliverance. Jesus *'drove out the spirits with a word'* (Matthew 8:16). Note that He didn't lead them out but drove them out. There's no point in saying, 'Please will you come out?' A command prayer of authority is required as the demon is challenged to leave the person in the name of Jesus (Acts 16:18).

Having claimed the protection of Christ's blood and bound the spirit, we don't then start arguing with it. When in a documentary Winston Churchill was asked what his answer was to a message sent to him by Hitler, he growled, 'I cannot reply to someone with whom I am not on speaking terms.' And when we are in the forefront of the battle the last thing we will do is send e-mails to the enemy.

Commanded to leave

Evil spirits must be told to go, even when they are not inhabiting a person's body, and if Jesus' name is used they have to bow to His authority. Some demons leave instantly when ordered to, like the one that mocked Jesus in the synagogue (Luke 4:35). Others only depart after a struggle, like Legion in the demoniac among the tombs (Mark 5:6–13). But all must leave eventually if they are commanded to in Jesus' name and if those people that they have gained a hold on have deliberately renounced and forsaken them. If you're unsure if a demon has left, one test is to ask the person to say 'Jesus is Lord'. Only the freed can say it (1 Corinthians 12:3).

It is wisest also to tell the spirits where to go, just as Jesus caused Legion to go into a herd of pigs (Mark 5:11–13). Chris and I always say to a demon, 'Go to where Jesus sends you' – and eventually it does. But direct ministry is necessary if actual possession is involved, not only because the person concerned also needs building up but because evil spirits can understand usually only what we say to them out loud. Although Satan has the power to drop thoughts into our minds, and although his agents pick up a certain amount of supernatural knowledge from him as we can from the Lord, they cannot automatically read our thoughts and they need to hear clearly each command we give in Jesus' name.

'Through praise shall the victory come'

Gloria was a young Huddersfield woman who came to coffee at our vicarage. Eventually she admitted her involvement in spiritism and the occult. She also shared she had been overtaken sometimes by trances. However, she wanted to be set free, and as a result arrangements were made for her to receive deliverance.

Several of us were involved in this, and we were shown early on by the Lord that *'through praise shall the victory come'*. We saw how the devil hates it when we praise God, and as the spirits in Gloria reacted to our worship and manifested themselves we cast them out in the name of Jesus. As each one left Christine experienced an identical release in her own body. One of them would not budge while being addressed in English but left rapidly when spoken to in a tongue! At one point Gloria shook violently as the evil spirits within her trembled when they listened to us reading the Scriptures in Revelation 20 all about the last judgement and Satan's final doom.

After two long days we came to a halt. We knew that Gloria was not completely free but we could get no further. So we rang up a friend in London and explained our problem. 'Have you cut her free from her ancestral line'? he enquired. We had not, and when we did this it worked. The way was now all clear for her complete deliverance. But even then the last evil spirit tried to pretend that it was not there! We were sure that it was, for the Lord has also built up a code of signs with us in this realm by which we knew more.

Finally I had a picture of a suitcase being shut down tightly and firmly locked, and the words 'The case is closed'. We all knew that it was, and so we praised the Lord for all that He had done.

After-care

Since a person has wittingly or unwittingly invited a spirit in by an act of his or her will, it will only go if by an act of will it is renounced along with the sin that originally attracted it to gain hold. An ounce of confession is worth a ton of exorcism, and Chris and I have discovered that the more the needy person co-operates in the deliverance ministry, the more easily the demon will leave.

If you are not sure and you seek Him, the Lord will show you when a person is completely free after exorcism ministry. Obviously it follows that there should be a change in the person in the coming days. If he manifested a spirit of violence during the ministry his violent tendencies should diminish afterwards. If a spirit of resentment was present, this may not be clear outwardly except for a possible sneer on his face, but in the days following the ministry it should soon become apparent that he expresses instead more of a forgiving, caring attitude, which the Lord will give him.

Afterwards we are responsible for seeing that the released captive is given care and fellowship, and that he or she keeps close to the Lord and away from those activities which might invite any other evil forces in by the back door to take the place of those demons who have left by the front door (Matthew 12:43–45). Then, as long as all present continue to claim protection, there is nothing to fear.

Practical discussion questions

1. What have you learned by seeing others do deliverance ministry?

2. How would you decide which type of deliverance to use?

3. A friend of yours has always 'been tied to his mother's apron strings'. How would you set about seeking to give him some help?

4. A witch wants to become a Christian. What steps might you take?

Tools

Question 31: Prayer and Fasting

What is the Value of Prayer and Fasting in Healing Ministry?

Throughout this book I have emphasised the value of prayer in the ministry. It is so vital that it is like the password needed for a computer. Without it everything is locked up from us, but once we use it a whole new world of possibilities is opened up for us.

Not everybody has grasped this truth. A vicar went into hospital and his Parochial Church Council, which was meeting the same week, instead of praying for his healing, sent him a message on parish notepaper: 'We wish you a speedy recovery by eleven votes to ten'!

Our votes can achieve little compared to our prayers. Some of us perhaps think of prayer especially in connection with our church prayer meeting, the communion service, or our daily 'quiet time'. But when Paul wrote, *'pray continually'* (1 Thessalonians 5:17) he was emphasising the need to be constantly in touch with the Lord, so that when we are faced with a situation requiring healing we shall be ready to pray accordingly, and expect to see great things.

The value of prayer

Let me underline some types of prayer that I have already mentioned.

The value of specific prayer

The first healing in the Bible came through specific prayer from a believing man:

> *'Then Abraham prayed to God, and God healed Abimelech, his wife and his slave girls so they could have children again ...'*
>
> (Genesis 20:17)

It is as we pray for specific people and needs that we are most likely to see things happen. The more specific we are, the more effective the healing often seems to be. The Lord has given us authority to speak to each specific obstacle, no matter if it is terminal cancer, marital break-up or mental depression.

Once we've named the problem, however, we have no need to dwell on it in our prayers. If I lay hands on a person's back and tell her pain to depart I may then continue praying while healing energy soaks in, but I turn my attention away from the pain and attempt to concentrate my prayers on the Lord and His plan for the person.

The value of positive prayer

There is nothing indefinite about Jesus' command to the fig tree: *'May you never bear fruit again!'* (Matthew 21:19). And the Lord is equally positive when it comes to the mountain that requires shifting: *'Go, throw yourself into the sea'* (Matthew 21:21).

One form of positive praying is to become 'two in agreement'. Sometimes Chris and I join hands and agree together for the healing of a person, a relationship, or some circumstances. We claim Jesus' promise that if two of us are agreed about anything on earth we can be sure it will be done in heaven (Matthew 18:19).

The value of united prayer

At one time I was puzzled as to why it made any difference if I prayed on my own for someone or if I prayed in conjunction with others of God's people. I had already discovered that it is not as if God thinks the more people that we can get praying, the more likely He is to answer our prayer! I then concluded that one main reason why united prayer is so powerful is not so much to do with God as with Satan. The devil can more easily distract or confuse one person praying on his or her own, while he finds it much harder to cause our thoughts to wander when we unite against him as an army.

When our son Paul, then aged ten, was rushed to hospital after being knocked unconscious by a car, as soon as we could we asked as many people as possible to pray for his definite recovery. The car had hit him full in the stomach and hurled him high into the air. As we looked at him unconscious in the hospital with all the tubes attached to different parts of his body, we knew that only prayer held the answer. We asked everyone to pray positively for a miracle. And a miracle there was, for five days later when Paul regained consciousness he had no brain damage or internal injuries. Along with medical care, united prayer had restored him.

The value of command prayers
It is sometimes argued, 'If Christians command, they are imposing their will upon a sick person.' But this need not be so if a sufferer appreciates what is happening. Jesus asked the invalid at the pool, *'Do you want to get well?'* before He commanded, *'Get up! Pick up your mat and walk'* (John 5:6–8). As we have seen, God's usual method is for a believer to command an affliction to leave the sick person, but occasionally the Christian may take authority over something in him or herself. A woman from East London wrote to us:

> 'I asked in Jesus' name if He'd cure me of a skin disease I'd endured for thirty years. I'd taken allergy pills for this after being told there was no cure. I followed your book [*Six Keys to Healing*] and used command prayers. To my amazement this terrible itching left me and, praise the Lord, hasn't come back! That was three months ago, and I haven't had to take another allergy pill.'

The value of thanksgiving prayers
Whenever Chris and I have ministered to sick people in a meeting the congregation have usually been worshipping the Lord. Such praise

- glorifies God
- uplifts people
- frightens Satan
- releases power.

We also praise Him as we pray with individuals, for part of the prayer of faith is thanking Him for the results *before* we view them. As when saying grace, we thank God for what we have not yet received. Once those who are sick have been ministered to, we encourage them to begin thanking the Lord that their healing has begun, and to take for granted that God will remove the problem in His way and time.

Jeremiah is a mournful prophet, yet every so often he breaks into a prayer of faith such as:

> *'Heal me, O Lord, and I shall be healed;*
> *save me and I shall be saved.'* (Jeremiah 17:14)

The secret of Jeremiah's confidence is then revealed: *'for you are the one I praise.'*

The value of guided prayer

Remember that prayer is not a one-way street. Therefore, as we saw in Section 6, as Christians ask the Lord, they may receive guidance about particular situations. At Redhill some prayed for a man who was mentally ill and suffering from cancer. One of them was shown Jesus walking along the garden path with another man their group did not know. They prayed about this and were given John 1:6: *'There came a man who was sent from God: his name was John.'* The man who was accompanying Jesus in the revelation turned out to be me!

But we cannot assume that everything that happens is an answer to prayer. A young Canadian's call to South America was confirmed, he said, when he spotted a bar of Brazil nut chocolate. But a friend remarked, 'It's a good job he didn't see a Mars bar!'

The value of persistent prayer

We don't have to beg and plead with God to heal, but we do need to persist until we see His answers to prayer. A man stood in a queue of people waiting to receive ministry. After he had been prayed for he felt no different so he joined the queue again. This he did fifteen times, and the fifteenth time he was satisfied! I am not suggesting that we need to do this, but at least that man was persistent! We give up too easily when discouraged. If we run into difficulties we should ask the Holy Spirit's guidance about the next step. Sometimes we ask the Lord about a sick person and then fail to wait for His reply. Persisting in prayer will mean looking for His answers to specific questions, especially as we get to know our Bibles and as we consult the Lord's people.

We need to remember as well that the healing service is like a surgery where Jesus is the doctor. It is open for just an hour or two at a time, and although we pray powerful prayers during this time they generally have to be quite brief ones. Many people need following up after these meetings. I have found that while I've spent on average between two and five minutes praying for someone in a meeting, I have seldom spent less than twenty minutes praying for a sick person in the relaxed surroundings of someone's home.

The value of sacrificial prayer

Chris and I once prayed, 'Lord, we shall do anything for You, we'll go anywhere with You.' This was a dangerous prayer to pray because God took us at our word, and through many painful experiences He moulded us and trained us for the ministry into which He led us.

A similar sort of prayer is necessary for those who would make progress in healing ministry, for the supreme test of ministering healing is the place the Lord occupies in it. Is He really put in charge? Does He decide things, or is He only called upon to help carry out the plans of others? Remember that we cannot walk in the flesh and the Spirit at the same time (Galatians 5:16), and only what is done in the Spirit will last (1 Corinthians 3:10–15).

The value of fasting

A number of churches hold days of prayer and fasting, especially when remembering church members who are seriously ill. The idea behind this is that some kinds of problem are only dealt with successfully when there is both concentrated prayer and fasting (Mark 9:29, AV). When Jesus said this was what was needed for the epileptic boy to be delivered, it's interesting that He did not then stop to pray and fast. But this is probably because He had already done so. Following the example of the Old Testament saints and John the Baptist, Christians can look above all to Jesus Himself as the one who urges them to pray and fast.

More alert

Fasting can be a valuable aid to healing, therefore, as it enables the Christian to be more alert and perhaps to give more time to prayer and listening to the Lord. Fasting should not be undertaken if a person is medically advised against it, or if there is any danger of anorexia nervosa. When Chris and I have been guided to follow a three- or four-day fast alongside giving the deliverance ministry, we've found towards the end of the second day to be the most difficult time not to eat. Once our bodies have passed this crucial low phase we've found the fasting has become much easier.

We may decide to fast either completely or partially. As we do this we can become clearer channels of healing because we shall be more alert to receive the clear-cut guidance that we often need. But when should we fast? It helps to have arranged seasons such as Lent when we can do it in conjunction with other people and concentrate on the disciplines of self-denial. But it's best if we seek God first and know when He deliberately calls the fast. For fasting too should be according to God's clock. If He says it's time to fast, we'll find it easier and more fruitful than if we decide to do it just because we think it might help (Isaiah 58:6–9).

If you ask Him He will show you the nature and the duration of the fast to be undertaken as well: part of a day, a whole day, several days, or – as in the case of two women I know – forty days!

Having arranged to minister deliverance to one woman, Chris was praying about it when she felt her face harden. 'What can it mean?' she asked me. 'Well, the only thing I can think of is when Jesus set His face like a flint to go to Jerusalem,' I replied thoughtfully (Luke 9:51). 'I feel sure I have to fast,' said Christine. Later we both recognised that the sign meant that she should be determined to see the fast through. When fasting my wife and I usually cut out all food but drink normally, and that's what we did in this case. We found this enhanced our minds, enabling us to receive more clear-cut guidance at every stage. We also needed a lot of persistence, as this particular fast lasted four whole days, the full duration of the ministry. But the woman, who was a hopeless captive to start with, was gloriously set free in the end.

Practical discussion questions

1. Compare the general prayers prayed for the sick in your church and specific ones with individuals. Do you see any difference?

2. Can you think of a situation at the moment in which you could help someone by becoming 'two in agreement'? (Matthew 18:19)

3. Is there an ongoing situation that is affecting someone in your church/group where people have given up instead of persisting?

4. Have you considered the possibility of holding a day of prayer and fasting for a sick member of your church? What can you do?

Question 32: Powerful Atmospheres
What Makes a 'Powerful' Meeting?

Let's get clear first what it is not. It is not necessarily a noisy meeting, nor one in which there is necessarily a lot of singing. In fact, some of the most powerful occasions I have encountered have been during times of quiet worship led by the Holy Spirit, and where there's an 'electric' atmosphere in which the Lord is moving. But, whatever the context, a powerful meeting is one in which the Spirit is manifestly moving so that the whole gathering is affected.

Powerful gatherings in the Bible

Throughout the Acts of the Apostles, in particular, we come across such gatherings. In Acts 2:1–4 the prayer meeting attended by 120 of the early Christians became a powerful one once there was the sound of the rushing mighty wind, the tongues like fire *'that separated and came to rest on each of them'*, and the baptism in the Spirit accompanied by speaking in tongues.

In Acts 4:31 another prayer meeting became manifestly powerful when *'the place where they were meeting was shaken. And they were all filled with the Holy Spirit and spoke the word of God boldly.'*

In Acts 8:18–19 Simon the great sorcerer saw such amazing things – probably speaking in tongues but possibly falling under God's power – that he offered the apostles money to buy their power.

In Acts 10:44–46 the Holy Spirit suddenly fell on Cornelius and his Gentile companions in such a manifest way that, once they also spoke in tongues, there could be no doubt about the power evident.

In Acts 16:25–34 it was when Paul and Silas were praising the Lord that the earthquake of AD 44 took place, enabling them to find freedom and their jailer and his household to find Jesus Christ. The fact that it happened right then was undoubtedly a miracle.

Powerful gatherings occurring today

Every so often today we see or hear of powerful incidents that are comparable to those I have mentioned from the Book of Acts.

When I first read Kathryn Kuhlman's books about people who had been healed through her ministry of the word of knowledge in America I was puzzled. Each testimony described how a sick one had usually been ministered to at least once elsewhere but shown no obvious improvement, yet once the individual attended her meeting he or she experienced a remarkable recovery. 'Why was this?' was the question I pondered.

I concluded it wasn't just because Kathryn was an exceptionally gifted lady. There must have been something about the atmosphere in her meetings that made a difference. Atmosphere is always very important in healing, whether in church, home, hospital or clinic, and in her meetings energy was being released in such powerful ways that this is one reason Kathryn had such powerful results.

One reason we *don't* see more powerful atmospheres like that is because, while all Christians are indwelt by the Holy Spirit, many churches still miss out on a *release* of the Spirit's power.

Power released through our mouths

One of the two main ways in which we can release power and thus create a powerful atmosphere is by opening our mouths in the Spirit. How can we see more healing power released in our churches? The Bible says,

> '... be filled with the Spirit. Speak to one another in psalms, hymns and spiritual songs. Sing and make music in your heart to the Lord, always giving thanks to God the Father for everything, in the name of our Lord Jesus Christ.'   (Ephesians 5:18–20)

When the Holy Spirit came at Pentecost prayer turned into praise (Acts 1:14; Acts 2:11), and such praise – not just singing and rejoicing, but Spirit-filled adoration – can release mighty power. Such healing power is also released through united prayer, the word spoken with authority, and through gifts of the Holy Spirit.

Power through praise
On one occasion Chris and I were attending a united service in Huddersfield Town Hall, and we were all singing 'Wind, wind, blow on me'. As we did, a rushing mighty wind swept along our row and knocked my wife to the floor! It was a powerful moment.

Power through prophecy
On another occasion in the seventies we faced much opposition in one church. There was a terrible atmosphere, and when we came to the laying-on-of-hands an uneasy silence fell. As Christine and I stood waiting to minister we sensed the Lord's power about to descend. Then I found myself speaking out in words of prophecy:

'What if I were to come back now? Would you all be ready? Is this how I wish to find you? Will you not all return to Me and accept the authority and ministries that I have placed among you? What if I were to come back now, and to find you like this?'

The power coming from these words was taking Chris's breath away. Then she heard a loud thud. It was her head hitting the stone chancel floor! When she got up she felt like a rag. She had to sit for the rest of the service, but felt totally relaxed and unhurt.

Power released through our hands

This is the other main way in which we can expect to see power manifested. God's touch has still its ancient power, and the power of touch is added to the power of prayer. When one lady discovered this she said to Chris and me, 'I wish I could gather my sick friends and relatives in this room – then you could touch them all.' So often Chris and I have found that once we lay hands on people in Jesus' name there is a powerful atmosphere and healing results.

Discharging the energy
Sometimes Christine's arms fill with power and it literally hurts her to heal. She has to discharge the energy into the needy person, an experience that she has sometimes compared to having a baby. At other times her hands will vibrate as she ministers to people.

One evening at Hildenborough we had already had the ministry of laying-on-of-hands and many people had received the touch of Jesus. But Chris was conscious that the power was still heavily upon her and that she needed to get rid of it. She was breathing heavily as she announced this to the congregation. In response a woman with a bad back, who had held back from coming forward, now took advantage of the invitation, and she was healed as a consequence.

After *It Hurts to Heal* was published, letters were received from all over the world. In some of these a number of Christians wrote to say they were so glad to read about these powerful incidents, and to realise that they were not the only ones to experience such 'strange' manifestations. But, if when the early Church prayed the building was shaken (Acts 4:31), we shouldn't be surprised if sometimes the Holy Spirit takes people off their feet or anoints their bodies in tangible ways, thus manifesting His glory. Such events can be present-day demonstrations of the Spirit's power (1 Corinthians 2:4). And He will come upon any of us in power if we just allow Him to.

Practical discussion questions

1. What manifestations of power can be found in the four Gospels?
2. How can a difficult atmosphere be changed to a congenial one?
3. Is the worship in your church something that God is bored with or that He delights in? What is limiting more release of power?
4. Have you opportunity right now to manifest the power of touch?

Question 33: Physical Sensations
Are Physical Sensations of Any Value?

Physical sensations can be of tremendous value as an aid to the ministry. They should never be regarded as an end in themselves but as a means by which God's power is manifested. I wonder if you've already noticed that there's one person in our family who particularly and frequently experiences these – it's Christine!

Christine's own experiences

There were three occasions in the early days that show us why Chris has particularly been blessed by the Lord in this manner.

The overflow
She comes from a family that suffers from sudden death syndrome, as a result of which half her brothers and sisters have died suddenly without warning and when they were perfectly healthy. After the second of these tragic deaths, Christine lost the reality of Jesus' presence and came to the point where she said, 'It's not enough just to believe any more, I must *know*!' This assurance came when she was baptised in the Spirit (Acts 1:5), at which point she asked the Lord that her experience of Him would be *physically tangible*. He then answered her prayer in a very physical way, as she felt the power of the Spirit flow up from her stomach and out through her mouth, causing her to speak in tongues. She literally experienced

John 7:38: *'out of his belly shall flow rivers of living water'* (AV). From that moment on she has often had physical sensations.

The thumps

The second occasion was when she wanted to manifest the gifts of the Spirit but did not know how to get started. She prayed that the Lord would show her how, and He did – rather unexpectedly! As we sat in a meeting in our parsonage in 1975 Chris suddenly felt an invisible person give her a thump in the stomach. It soon came at regular intervals, while her tongue was moving inside her mouth. Nervously she gave her first gift of tongues to the group.

From then on 'the thumps', as we affectionately call it, became a sign that God wanted Chris to speak out a tongue, not just at meetings but in all kinds of contexts. He still often speaks to us in this way, even in the most mundane situations. Chris will give the tongue until she stops thumping, and I will interpret what the Lord wishes to say to us. Sometimes He even breaks into our conversation about everyday things to speak to us in this way.

The hills

The third occasion was when we lived at Huddersfield and the Lord showed her to get up early each morning and go into the hills to pray. One day there He anointed her and she felt full of His power. She started to pray aloud and as the Holy Spirit took hold of her words she realised she was praying an extraordinary prayer. She longed that He should possess her in every part, and she found herself naming every outer and inner organ of her body, ending with her red and white corpuscles. At the end she seemed to merge with the Lord in a very awesome experience. She sat on a huge rock to recover, astonished to find her prayer had lasted three hours!

Signs that we feel

Bathed in heat

There are many feelings we experience which are also signs of the Lord's power. Heat is one of the commonest, and it usually refers to something positive while cold can indicate something nega-tive. Sometimes the Lord will bathe the top half of my body in warmth. This may be His way of nudging me to do something, it may confirm to me something that He is saying, or He may simply do it because He loves me! When Jesus was anointed with the Holy Spirit after His baptism, it was not only for the ministry He would exercise but in recognition that He was God's Son (Luke 3:21–23). Sometimes God anoints a Christian simply because the Father loves to bless His sons and daughters (Romans 8:15–16). In every instance we must not rely on such feelings at the expense of faith, but they can prove tremendously encouraging to us in the healing ministry.

Feelings as confirmation

There are many other ways in which God may confirm the rightness of something through physical sensations, for Jesus cannot only touch our bodies through the laying-on-of-hands, He can anoint us anywhere, any time. My wife and I were once viewing some articles in a furniture shop when the Lord's anointing came upon Chris and she was bathed in His power. A lady in one of our London meetings, however, who was not used to this sort of thing, suddenly felt a movement upon her stomach (she had stomach trouble). Later she told Chris and me, 'I went outside to walk it off.' 'You don't walk *off* the Spirit,' we laughed, 'you walk *in* Him!' (see Galatians 5:25).

Physical promptings

I've already mentioned how sometimes, too, it is physical sensations that prompt us into knowing what God is doing in healing. One night at Hildenborough I felt warmth on my eyes and announced that the Lord was touching eyes. A woman present claimed this by faith and was healed of glaucoma and in-growing eyelashes. On other occasions I've had similar promptings to pray for sick people. One afternoon I had a boiling-hot foot and didn't know what it meant. Chris soon reminded me of a parishioner who had foot trouble. Then, when I had pressure on my nose, we knew we were to pray for someone else who had had an operation on his nose. Very occasionally I feel a warmth in my right ear. This, we've come to learn, means that there is unhelpful gossip going on about our ministry, so we claim the victory over it. More than once we have discovered that there was gossip taking place at the exact moment that I received the sign.

Signs that we see

I've also already described how God has built up some codes with us by which we are able to discern when the enemy is at work. One that Christine experiences is being hit by a sense of blackness.

Seeing blackness

This happened once when she laid hands on Hazel, whom we had met on holiday at a hotel in Devon. Hazel had enquired, 'Will you pray for me? I need God's help as my husband often goes into violent and uncontrollable rages.' Once Chris saw blackness she recognised that Satan was in this situation. Immediately she took authority over him in the name of Jesus. It transpired that Hazel's husband Bob had even ridden a bicycle over her while she was pregnant, so it was not surprising that Satan was at work. But after the ministry Bob went for help to a healing mission, and came to know the Lord.

Gasping for breath

Sometimes other people see physical signs upon us. At the end of one meeting in our Huddersfield vicarage God's power was still mightily at work. One lady who had hesitated to ask for ministry found herself being propelled forwards across the room to us by an unseen force. At the same time Chris found herself gasping for breath, as if she was struggling against a rushing mighty wind! The lady stood in front of Chris and me, and we laid hands on her. As people left to go home, another woman drew Chris to one side and remarked, 'When you were ministering tonight I saw something that looked like electricity flashing out of your fingers!'

Signs that we do

The Holy Spirit also causes us to perform signs with our bodies.

Acted signs

Every so often the Lord will cause one of us to act out a sign. He uses our bodies – and particularly Chris's – to act like a code. Sometimes if He wants to say no to something, she finds her head shaking, or perhaps her eyes closing, or even her foot stamping. Ezekiel had to eat a scroll, draw a map on a brick and dig through a wall, so we do not count these signs as bizarre but as another way in which God loves to guide. Helpful though they are, these signs only occur every so often, and we have learned to rely upon the inner witness of the Spirit, not on the signs.

One afternoon Chris found herself with one hand up in the air drawing a circle. She knew she was to write a letter, and we soon ascertained that it was to a lady who served as a reader who was shaped just like a ball! The Lord has a great sense of humour.

Resting in the Spirit

One of the things that can happen when we yield ourselves to the Holy Spirit is that we enter temporarily into a different level of consciousness. We're not unconscious but 'resting in the Spirit' (I prefer this term to 'slain in the Spirit', as the person is far from dead!). Under certain circumstances our brainwaves change from regular beta ones to alpha ones. This can happen through harmful experimentation with hard drugs or transcendental meditation, but it can also happen during Spirit-filled worship or contemplative meditation upon the Lord, and under the ministry of laying-on-of-hands. In particular, we may often rest in the Spirit after falling under God's power. A number of people fell under this power in the Bible (Acts 9:4; Revelation 1:17), and the Jewish Temple Police fell backwards in the Garden of Gethsemane when Jesus replied to His accusers by using the powerful name of God 'I am' (John 18:6).

Resting in the Spirit on the floor is now extremely widespread and seems to be linked less with particular ministries as with powerful atmospheres such as the ones I was describing in the last chapter. It has taken place in great evangelistic crusades and also at Anglican theological colleges where the staff have been laying on hands. We should beware of aiming to fall, but if we resist the power we may miss out on a blessing. God will not compel anyone to fall who is tense or resistant, and no minister can force it to happen as a by-product of the ministry. Resting in the Spirit does not necessarily mean a person is healed or baptised in the Spirit: it's simply a sign that God's power has been released and that Jesus is working in our midst (Mark 16:20).

While on the floor people are usually at their most relaxed, so God may be ministering to them at deeper levels of their subconscious quite apart from the ministry we have given them. Many have been convicted of sin, drawn closer to Jesus, seen visions, or found fresh strength for living, and these blessings have shown in the radiance of their faces when they have returned to their places afterwards. Falling under the power sometimes occurs when no one is laying hands on people and when those concerned are also at a distance from the ministers. Chris and I always point everyone beyond such experiences to our mighty God, and give Him the glory.

It can be undignified if people keel over while kneeling, so in our own ministry at meetings we have usually asked them to stand while we have laid hands on them, and have some catchers on hand to lower them gently to the floor. This is purely for reassurance, as no harm has come to people who have fallen without catchers. But these stewards can also look after spectacles, ear pieces and crutches while the ministry is proceeding, and be prepared to help people to their feet again when they are eventually ready.

Practical discussion questions

1. What can Chris's experience teach us about physical signs?
2. Have you had experience of feelings (a) prompting you to act? (b) confirming something as right? (c) assuring of God's love?
3. If while praying during a meeting you saw a picture of an arm supported in a sling, what might you proceed to say and do?
4. How can you reassure someone who fears falling under the power?

Outlook

Question 34: No Condemnation

As a Therapist I'm Shunned by Other Christians. What Can I Do?

'The outlook for tomorrow is showers with bright periods . . . and that's the end of the weather forecast.' Outlook is the subject of this last main section of the book, and the outlook for us and those we share healing with also depends to some extent upon the 'whether' forecast – whether we'll go forward in obedience to God.

First, we explore this question about what the therapist shunned by other Christians should do, and here there are three factors to consider.

The type of people concerned

Who are these Christians who are ostracising the therapist because he or she is a complementary practitioner? Most likely they are others in his or her own church. Perhaps there's no difference in their basic understanding of the faith, but because of ignorance, misunderstanding or fear, the shutters come down once it is known that the individual is involved in therapy.

The dogmatic

The first type of Christian that may be involved here is the one who dogmatically states that all therapy is of the devil, or at least that it is wrong for the believer. Often this attitude is the result of ignorance. Now it is not a sin to be ignorant, but it becomes a sin when such individuals insist that they are not! In the many cases I have encountered, these people have frequently picked up their ideas from something they have read or heard, perhaps one statement only by a Christian writer or speaker, and accepted that as gospel truth which then becomes a part of their own beliefs and attitudes.

Alternatively, it may be due to misunderstanding. When a Christian lady once heard that Christine's hands vibrated, the woman became horrified and cried out apprehensively, 'Spiritualists do that!' She was assuming that, because this was experienced by people who did not please the Lord, the experience must be wrong in itself. But we have seen how many things can be used for good or evil, and we also know that the cure for abuse is not misuse but right use.

Christian practitioners, therefore, needn't be ashamed of enthusing about how God is using them. They can make clear that they too love the Lord, and that they are as much against the occult as their critics.

The anxious

There are other people who again only have a vague idea of what is involved in complementary therapies but who become worried about the possibility that anything to do with it could lead to Satan gaining a hold upon them, and that perhaps somehow an evil spirit could be transferred to them simply by their coming into contact with anyone involved in this area. Their attitude is consequently one of steering clear of everything that hints of complementary medicine, believing that even osteopathy is a 'doorway to danger'.

Something to make clear here when possible is that dualism is a false concept, that Satan has nowhere near the power that God has and that Christians under God's protection have nothing to fear.

The sceptical

This group of Christians especially includes some doctors and others who will not accept anything in complementary medicine unless it has been scientifically proved to their satisfaction. Among them are those, for example, who are not prepared to accept that there is sufficient evidence for different energy systems within the human body, so they write off most popular therapies. They need to be reminded that much in orthodox medicine and in Christian healing can also not yet be proved in black and white.

It takes time for people to change their minds, and we must be gentle and patient in dealing with their different attitudes, but perhaps we can sometimes ask such people questions to help make them think, such as 'Why are more Christians not healed?'

'Why should the devil have all the best cures?' and 'Why, if pagan roots are wrong, do those who question origins glibly accept doctors?'

When we cannot speak to our critics personally we may be able to make use of tapes, testimonies and positive literature compiled by other Christians, especially doctors and therapists themselves.

The attitude we should take

Loving

Of course, the therapists who are shunned by other Christians may have no opportunity to put their side of the case. But, even when they do, it's important to love – not condemn – those who oppose us. When one person asked how he should treat such people, he was told, 'Do what Stephen did: love them to death!' (Acts 7:59–60). This does not mean we shall not sometimes offend people: by entering Zacchaeus' house Jesus offended the scribes (Luke 19:5–7). But in the end it's love that causes people to change their minds.

In Breath we have a policy of no condemnation. Since Paul writes, *'there is now no condemnation for those who are in Christ Jesus'* (Romans 8:1), we believe we've no right to condemn others. Even when someone confesses to me a murder – which occasionally happens – I obviously don't condone the sin but neither do I go on to condemn the person.

I prefer to leave the judging to God. And if we take this attitude when faced with difficult people, God will do one of three things:

1. *judge them*: by allowing them to suffer and thus learn a lesson;
2. *move them*: away from the area, so they are no longer a problem;
3. *change them*: in a genuine way, so they are different towards us.

Understanding

In parts of East Africa, when a native greets another with, 'How are you?' the reply is, 'I am if you are.' It is important in dealing with those Christians who see things differently from us that we treat them as equals and accept each one of them as they are, with unconditional love. When conversing with them, this means starting where they are and putting ourselves in their shoes. We each need to become a listener, allowing for the person's personality, age and mood. John the Baptist was not jealous of Jesus, another pastor, and in the same way we relate in a spirit of co-operation rather than competition.

Forgiving

The other thing Jesus can help us do is forgive such people for ostracising us. But it's not always easy to forgive when we have been wronged. Chris and I led a young couple to put their trust in Christ but it soon became clear that the wife had committed adultery. When Chris encouraged the husband to forgive her, he at first refused, saying he could never do so. But when Chris explained how God had forgiven him when he didn't deserve it, he forgave his wife with the help of the Lord. At the very same moment he went down on the floor under the power of God. On some occasions Jesus has even enabled such people not only to forgive but also to forget, as the most painful memories are erased.

The needs of the therapist

But the complementary practitioner may be thinking, 'It's all very well being reminded what my attitude should be, but what help can others give me right now while these Christians are shunning me?'

Encouragement

First, let me encourage such a person by assuring you you are not alone. Elijah was once desperate and suicidal, partly because he was afraid of Queen Jezebel and partly because he had a lack of self-worth: '*I am no better than my ancestors*' (1 Kings 19:4). God reassured him with the fact that he was not alone. There were seven thousand others like him who didn't worship Baal (1 Kings 19:18). Be encouraged now by the fact that we are in touch with hundreds of Christian therapists in addition to those on our Register, and that there are probably thousands of these. Whatever Christians close to you may say, there are people out there who feel called just as you do to be involved in complementary medicine. Many, perhaps like you, feel isolated and rejected. But the Lord told us once through prophecy that His heart yearns for each one, and He is grieved by the way in which some have been treated by believers.

Fellowship

There is no need for the rejected therapists to feel completely alone. There will be those on the National Register of Christian Therapists who, I'm sure, would love you to have fellowship with them. There are also Christian fellowships within some of the different disciplines involved, such as the Osteopaths' Christian Fellowship.

Support

PACT exists partly to give support to complementary practitioners, and especially through the Register to link up like-minded people. There are also some natural health centres staffed completely by Christians, such as Newlands Park Natural Health Centre, Sydenham, South London, and Christian healing centres in which complementary therapists take part, such as Green Pastures at Poole in Dorset.

We've found that many of the questions at our healing meetings are about PACT, and in turn many people who attend PACT events ask for healing ministry. And a familiar need is for healing of hurts suffered by practitioners because of hostile Christians. One aromatherapist at Oxford confessed, 'I was once very hurt by Christians calling me evil.' But such people have sometimes been able to receive deep ministry as we have sought, like the Good Samaritan, to bandage their wounds one by one (Luke 10:34). The rejected therapist is freed from painful memories and given new strength and confidence to cope with the situation in his or her home area. So healing ministry is recommended for all such people, and no one need feel abandoned entirely if he or she takes advantage of it.

Practical discussion questions

1. You are faced with a worried member of your church or group who is frightened of complementary medicine. How can you help?

2. Jesus' new commandment was not just to love one another but *'as I have loved you'* (John 13:34). How does this apply in your situation?

3. Is there someone you find difficult to forgive? Can others help?

4. Someone you know is being shunned and rejected by several other Christians, for whatever reason. How can your church reassure him or her?

Question 35: **Christian Involvement**
Should Christians Distance Themselves from New Agers?

Soon after Sir Cliff Richard became a Christian, some believing friends tried to persuade him to give up show business to concentrate just on singing at gospel events. They viewed the whole entertainment business as a 'worldly' activity that fell far short of the standards required for the people of God. But Cliff could never have reached so many people for the Lord outside that world as he could within it. He has been able to maintain his singing profession while everyone clearly knows about his beliefs.

Involvement and separation

There has always been a tension among Christian people as to how far to be separated from the world as different people, yet how far to be involved as witnesses for Christ. Jesus said of His disciples, *'They are not of the world'*, but He also said, *'I have sent them into the world'* (John 17:16, 18).

Insulated wires

In the mid-twentieth century many Christians thought it wrong to visit 'worldly' places such as theatres, cinemas, dance halls and pubs, and women were forbidden to use make-up. The worry was that people who were not strong in faith would be swayed in the wrong direction. Nowadays it is recognised that the only way to reach many people in such establishments is to go there. We are to be like insulated wires, running through all kinds of places while protected from contact with those things that would harm us. We have already seen that Paul taught it was permissible for people to eat food that had been offered to idols, if they could do this in good conscience and without causing spiritual harm to others.

An exciting mission field

It's precisely because the church has distanced itself from some sections of the community that it has caused people to look elsewhere for help. They have especially seen it lacking in spiritual power and joy, in a true sense of community, in an immediate experience of God, and confused over faith and morals. Many

New Agers think of Christianity and the church as being 'old-hat' and out of touch. The New Age movement, therefore, fills a spiritual vacuum for many.

But a nutrition consultant in Essex wrote to us stating that she saw New Age as 'a challenging but exciting mission field, where the lost will not be reached if Christians hold back in fear.' If we retreat from involvement in the field of alternative medicine New Agers and others with whom we disagree will predominate in it. And a Christian influence is needed within it to balance other ideas. Nor can we expect to win New Age people for the Lord unless some Christians go to them, for as Paul wrote, *'how can they hear without someone preaching to them?'* (Romans 10:14). And the preaching need not be in sermons: it's as we gossip the gospel that they will hear it.

Negative and positive

Praying and speaking against New Age establishments is not enough, though some people are only able to pray. Nor is it any good just being negative: a *positive* approach is required with the New Age Movement, as it is with complementary therapies. The wrong approach is to confront New Agers with a challenge to reject their spirituality totally. Jesus met ordinary people where they were. We shall want to deal lovingly and gently with any differences that arise, but recognise that many New Age people are seeking God – though they wouldn't see it like that – and shouldn't be condemned for that!

Getting alongside them

If we are to get alongside New Agers we need to be approachable and be able to put people at ease. It may simply be in the course of our daily work or leisure that we come across them, and then we can take the opportunity to witness for Christ when it arises.

Seeking for reality
Malcolm was a lecturer at the British School of Osteopathy while Chris was training there. One day Chris was talking to a patient in the clinic and remarked that we did healing. Malcolm overheard, and soon got talking over coffee with Chris. It transpired that he was seeking for reality in his life, and he had already sought for

this in Buddhism and recently in the New Age movement, but all without success. He read *It Hurts to Heal* with avid interest. Then, desperate and eager, he travelled eighty miles from Basingstoke to attend our meeting at Hildenborough, where he received laying-on-of-hands and was greatly blessed but was full of questions.

Chris and I invited Malcolm back to our house, where he relaxed while we talked and prayed with him until 2.00 a.m. Suddenly things made sense to him and he said, 'I know it up here now [pointing to his head] but I don't feel it down here [pointing to his heart].' A little later, however, he said, 'Now I feel it in here!' He had come to know Jesus, and with our encouragement he shortly after this joined a church in Hampshire that took him under its wing.

Indrag or infiltration?
When Chris and I left the comparative isolation of the vicarage and first lived in a council house, what a difference it made! Neighbours were swiftly converted, healed and filled with the Holy Spirit, and the whole housing estate was soon talking about it!

It reminded us that we are more likely to win people to Christ if we go where they are rather than wait for them to come to us. The invitation method of evangelism is still valid, but these days indrag is not enough. Outreach is essential (Matthew 28:19–20).

So when it comes to New Agers I do not suggest just inviting them to church meetings, however attractive these may be. They first have to be convinced that we have something worthwhile to offer, and this is only likely to happen if we get alongside them and share. Once again we may use testimonies, tapes and liter-ature to help prepare the way, but face-to-face communication is most fruitful.

It was because one therapy student had read one of our books that she became interested in Christianity, though she was at first hesitant to commit herself, confessing, 'I was frightened I might become a Christian accidentally!' It was when she and her husband were personally invited to an informal evening at a local church that they responded to the invitation of Christ. Another therapy student, who also read the book, had noticed something different about Chris, and stopped her one day as she was about to drive off in our car. 'I don't know how to put this, Chris,' said the woman, 'but I'd like to join a religion or something.' She was invited back to our home and she too came to trust in the Lord.

Reality and relevance

A starting-point for conversation with New Agers may be sharing common interests or responding to news items about health or the environment. Many of them are also looking for reality, and it is here that 'power evangelism' speaks more than just proclamation. If we accompany what we have to share with references to healing and miracles, we are on subjects that will often interest them. Better still, if they see that we demonstrate the love of Jesus, this can speak to their hearts:

> *'By this all men will know that you are my disciples, if you love one another.'*   (John 13:35)

Some churches are so well known for the loving welcome they give that outsiders are in effect saying, 'See how these Christians love one another!' When we first started Breath and held gatherings in our home, a number of newcomers were converted before they had hardly heard anything said about Jesus. They were so bowled over by the love and care.

The other need is that we make Christianity relevant to the New Ager as to the ordinary person in the street. A window of an East End London church contained the inscription 'Glory to God in the highest' (Luke 2:14). But one day a little urchin threw a stone that nicked out the letter 'e' and then it read 'Glory to God in the high st'. Jesus got through to people on their wavelength. For some older people we may need a 'Radio 3' wavelength and the Authorised Version, while for some younger ones we need a 'Radio 1' approach and modern English. The message is the same, and only the Holy Spirit can open their eyes. But the methods will vary.

Key questions and truths

Some key questions to ask when conversing with New Agers include:

- 'Do you have a philosophy of life?'
- 'Do you have a faith of any kind?'
- 'Are you involved in any spiritual activities?'
- 'What do you think about … Christ?' (Matthew 22:42).

If they are in particular need we may add:

- 'Have you thought of trying Christian healing?'
- 'How did your problems begin?'
- 'Have you received help before?'

Some key truths we can seek to convey include the uniqueness of Christ (John 14:6), justification by faith, not works (Ephesians 2:8–9), assurance of eternal life (1 John 5:13), and that wholeness includes getting right with God through repentance and faith in Christ.

Where do we draw the line?

We should only get involved with New Agers when the Holy Spirit leads us to, and we must have no direct involvement with the dark areas, such as those explored in answer to Question 26. If we are unsure, we again need to obtain confirmation or hold back until we *are* sure. Worship and evangelism are not levels on which Christians can work with New Agers, but we *may* work with them to a certain extent on levels associated with health, the environment and social work.

Health shows and psychic fairs

However, I'm sometimes asked whether it is safe for the Christian to attend health shows and similar functions. It is again, I believe, a superstitious idea to think that we shall become automatically contaminated or harmed by going to such events. Chris represented osteopathy at one such show, and we noticed that some stalls at it were New Age and questionable from the Christian point of view, but it made no difference to what Chris was able to do.

When I visited one Psychic Fair people were really interested in Christian healing, and I believe such events give opportunities for evangelism. At one of them a stall next to a Christian one had to close because it couldn't cope with the power of Christ! In addition, half a dozen people became Christians as a result. However, we need to claim God's protection when entering these establishments, and we often need back-up. Ask other Christians to pray for you as ambassadors for Christ (2 Corinthians 5:20). Among other things you should be able to convey that the Church offers healing, and to share why it is worth accepting this offer.

Using your ministry

Each one of us needs to ascertain what is his or her main ministry in relation to the New Age movement. Every Christian has a ministry: how can mine be used in this area? With which people and on what levels is God calling me to be involved? Am I to pray only? To write letters? To back others? To train to become a complementary therapist? To reach out by going into some New Age establishments?

Jesus once told a story about a great banquet, and how everyone who was first invited made excuses for not attending. One used his possessions as an excuse, another his work, another his family (Luke 14:8–24). Nowadays when Jesus sends His Christian servants to bring needy people to His feast of wholeness, it is not only those who are invited who make excuses: it is those who are sent. And it is still possessions, work and family that we mention most. All these may be good in themselves, but how shall New Agers hear without a preacher? And maybe He desires that preacher to be you.

Practical discussion questions

1. Are there New Age establishments in your area for you to go to?
2. How are most people becoming Christians in your area – through invitations, conversations, proclamations or demonstrations?
3. Have you made any excuses for not getting involved with people?
4. Is your church on people's wavelength? Can it be more relevant?

Question 36: Dynamic Vision

How Do You See the Future In Terms of Healing and Wholeness?

We have now come quite a long way in our exploration of healing and therapies, yet there still lies a great ocean before us that waits to be plumbed. That is why I believe we need a dynamic vision.

Catching the vision

> *'Where there is no vision, the people perish.'*
>> (Proverbs 29:18, AV)

A vision is a picture of what we would like the future to hold. Even if I never achieve my vision, pursuing it can give me purpose and incentive. Robert Browning wrote, 'A man's reach should exceed his grasp, or what's a heaven for?' So the important thing is to aim high. If I aim low I miss my target by a long way, but if I aim high I am more likely to come near it. As my vision increases, so will my expectancy, and vice-versa. Outdoors we can all see a horizon. If we ever reach that horizon we see another, further in the distance. Similarly, if I ever achieve my vision I seek another, otherwise I tend to stay still in my expectations. So I would encourage you to pursue your vision as it widens.

Vision and action

I have a vision for the future of healing and wholeness which I believe is part of God's perfect plan for us. As I explain this vision in this last chapter, I hope that, having read this book, you will catch something of the same dynamic vision. For such a vision can only be achieved when Christian leaders, doctors and therapists, along with many other people, catch something of the vision and endeavour to make it come to pass. And such a vision is useless without action. Joel Barker made this memorable remark:

> 'Vision without action is merely a dream.
> Action without vision just passes the time.
> Vision with action can change the world.'

The future of complementary therapies

We saw in the Prologue that in Breath we were called by the Lord to blaze a trail in this area, and that would mean being pioneers. Pioneers are often not recognised during their lifetime. Onlookers may think they are strange or eccentric. It may only be many years later that they are honoured. And as humble pioneers in connection with complementary medicine we are not expecting an easy ride. We expect there will be some criticism of this book from those who take a different viewpoint from us. Nevertheless I'm hopeful that part of my vision for this area can be achieved before very long.

1. I should love the acceptable therapies to be more widely used
During recent years this has already begun to take place, since a substantial proportion of the UK population visits therapists. It is my hope that this will continue to increase, as so many more people could benefit. All the signs point to the fact that, as more publicity is given to complementary medicine, it is here to stay.

2. I should love all these therapies to be made more use of abroad
At the moment there are some countries where therapies of every kind abound, such as in Western Europe, and others where people have hardly ever heard of them, such as in parts of Africa. The ways in which they are organised are different in every country but the need to embrace their healing remedies remains the same.

3. I should love to see more research into complementary medicine
The research which I have mentioned in this book is only really the tip of an iceberg compared to what could be undertaken if we saw more time, money and resources made available. Since these therapies tend to match remedies not just to symptoms but to the client's overall needs, each may have to be tested in a different way. But such research could reassure many people who are sceptical.

4. I should love to see much more regulation of these therapies
Following in the footsteps of osteopathy and chiropractic, there are some other therapies seeking statutory regulation and others still that will need to. When all practitioners are included on the national register for their particular therapy, we can all have more confidence that those who treat us are safe and competent.

5. I should love to see more doctors accept complementary medicine
There is still a fair proportion of orthodox medical people who resist or ignore the complementary scene. Some are only likely to accept it when they see more scientific evidence for its efficacy and others are too engrossed in their own work to afford it much thought. Only a small proportion of doctors even refer patients to

osteopaths – they are used to sending them to physiotherapists. Something that may help here is balanced writing on the subject of therapy by those doctors who have first-hand experience of it. Also helping to pave the way for greater acceptance are the many younger doctors already relating to the complementary scene, the moves being made to take some therapists into the National Health Service, and integration of orthodox and complementary practices.

6. I should love more Christians to accept complementary therapies
This book is a small step in encouraging them to do so. But again there are many who at present reject therapy out of hand or hesitate to become involved. The acronym *nose* reminds us of their main reasons:

- New Age associations
- Origins that are questionable
- Scientific difficulties
- Emphasis on energy

There is a great need for more Christians to study the subject, for experienced leaders and Christian therapists to write about it from a positive angle, and for churches to make it a part of the teaching they offer people in healing and wholeness. My prayer is that the climate of opinion, which is already gradually changing, will continue to gather speed.

7. I should love people to exercise more discernment in this area
While some Christian people oppose the whole complementary field, the opposite is happening in the world in general. In many cases people are not concerned about the rightness of a therapy as long as it works for them. I hope that the warnings in this book about practices which we believe to be harmful will be taken notice of.

8. I should love more Christians to be involved with the therapies
The Lord is calling more believers to train as natural therapists but still more are needed if the Christian influence and message is to make sufficient impact on the complementary medicine world to balance up what others are doing. There is also a need for more Christians to pray for and reach out to practitioners and clients.

Integrated health care

I should also love to see more integration of health care provided in the orthodox and complementary medical fields. The Integrated Healthcare Initiative is a proposed way forward, led by the Prince of Wales' Foundation together with the NHS Alliance and National Association for Primary Care. Its aims include carrying out comprehensive surveys of the provision required, including an assessment of the needs of the professionals seeking integration. There is an undertaking to assess current health needs that are being poorly met by conventional medicine, to give comprehensive advice on the best practice envisaged, and to undertake a review of international initiatives in integrated service provision. And five integrated health care projects in primary care trusts around the UK have been acting as pilot studies to determine how best to deliver alternative therapies alongside conventional medicine. These pilot schemes all involve well-resourced units and networks able to study and teach, and provide relevant therapist services.

The future of healing ministry

I should love to see the recommendations of reports like *A Time to Heal* put into practice in every church and Christian group, so that healing takes the important place Jesus gave it in His work.

1. I should love more fellowships to launch into healing ministry
Although far more churches now have such a ministry, many do not. In some it is regarded as something just for those interested in that sort of thing, just as some people might be interested in a particular missionary society while others are not. In many other fellowships the leaders have not introduced such a ministry since they do not see themselves as having the gift of healing. In other cases there is a desire to do something but there is hesitation on the part of the leaders because they are not sure how to start, or they may experience some apprehension about what they could get themselves involved in. I should love to help more of such fellowships, either by first discussing the possibilities with those most interested or by conducting a simple healing service to show how it is done.

2. I should love more churches to make healing a central ministry
In many churches it is not possible to offer this ministry at the main Sunday service as the people who normally attend do not

appear ready or willing for it. At the moment, therefore, these fellowships offer ministry on other occasions, such as at midweek communion services or with prayer groups. I rejoice that these are available, but healing will never make the full impact that the Lord intends it to unless it becomes a central ministry. Leaders, therefore, should endeavour to work towards this aim, and again I can encourage them in ways to do this, if they would like me to. Ideally the ministry should be part of the main Sunday service so that the whole body of Christ met there can take part in it.

3. I should love to see healing made a wider part of church life
It is thrilling when at every church activity someone is prepared to pray with anyone in need, and this is often not too difficult to arrange. Smaller churches may find it hard to obtain all the personnel to follow up people in their homes, but ideally this is a requirement of the wider ministry. When healing ministry is tackled ecumenically more people can be available with different gifts, and I should love to see more interdenominational meetings at which ministry is offered, such as we've been doing in Breath.

4. I should love to see all Christians share healing in some way
The concept of every-member ministry is still foreign to a number of churches, with the consequence that healing is seen solely as something to be offered by the leaders. While leaders need to get involved as much as they can, the churches that are making most progress in this area are the ones where the members are encouraged and taught to minister to one another, so that there is a constant flow of healing love and power streaming through the congregation.

5. I should love to see healing become more part of everyday life
If, however, we only cater for the needs of those who worship with us we are missing out on the tremendous opportunities that arise in our everyday circumstances. I long to see the touch of Jesus offered more and more in informal situations at home, at work, at school and in leisure contexts. This is where healing can also be used as an important point of contact for evangelism, and where, as we share our testimonies, we can impact on the wider community.

6. I should love to see more people renewed in the Spirit's power
We have seen what a difference it can make when Christians and churches are filled with the Holy Spirit and on fire for the

Lord. Healing should result as a natural consequence of this experience.

7. I should love to see the gifts of the Spirit more widely used

I hope I have also made clear in this book just what a difference spiritual gifts can make to the effectiveness of healing ministry when they are used wisely. They are equipment we cannot do without.

8. I should love to see more signs and wonders done in Jesus' name

It would be disappointing if we observed lots of healings but no genuine miracles. I should love to see more of both, especially because these can help point unbelievers to Christ, as they did in Bible times. I believe that if we are faithful to our commission we can claim Jesus' promise to Nathanael for ourselves: *'You shall see greater things than these'* (John 1:50, RSV).

Healing of the churches

The night before He died Jesus prayed for His disciples, *'that all of them may be one'* (John 17:21). His prayer was answered on the Day of Pentecost, when we find,

> *'All the believers were together and had everything in common.'*
> (Acts 2:44)

But it was not long before disunity and disharmony crept back into the Church, and throughout the centuries there has been the need for healing of relationships among both different fellowships and different individuals. I do not believe we can expect uniformity of worship and organisation among different denominations, but I do believe we should:

> *'Make every effort to keep the unity of the Spirit through the bond of peace.'*   (Ephesians 4:3)

Sometimes the introduction of healing ministry brings to light divisions that already exist, but with gentle and able leadership these can often be addressed. I look forward to hearing of more and more reconciliations as Christians recognise that we are *'all one in Christ Jesus'* (Galatians 3:28). This does not mean that we gloss over our differences, but that we may make them subservient to our main work of serving the Lord.

Healing of the nations

When we read, *'the leaves of the tree are for the healing of the nations'* (Revelation 22:2), we can be sure that this too is part of God's perfect will. But the Bible is quite clear that we cannot expect complete healing of the world till after Jesus returns in body. The prophecies in it that are still unfulfilled speak of a world that is going to get worse, not better, as the current wave of wars and terrorism indicate. According to the famous Bible Code and many of the signs we see around us, we are already living in what the Bible calls *'the end of ... days'* (Daniel 12:12). In particular, as we look at the Holy Land and the Middle East we can see events mounting up towards the final things God has foretold.

But this should not discourage us, nor cause us to draw back from praying for healing of nations when that appears a possibility. As new Christians and new churches are appearing every day, as more people are being reached with the gospel than ever before because of the speed of communications and travel, and as a spiritual revival springs up every so often, so we see healing happening on a wider scale. And we can expect this to continue till Jesus comes.

No more need of healing

There is coming a time when there will be no more need of healing, or the other gifts of the Holy Spirit (1 Corinthians 13:8). That time will be when *'I shall know fully, even as I am fully known'* (1 Corinthians 12:12). I'm looking forward to the new heaven and new earth where *'There will be no more death or mourning or crying or pain'* (Revelation 21:4). Whatever our vision for healing and wholeness, this is what all who trust in Jesus for salvation can ultimately look forward to: bodies, minds, and spirits made perfect in glory.

How you can help

You, the reader, may feel that any contribution you make to healing and wholeness is small and insignificant, but it's as we each play our part that we can help to see the vision fulfilled. One way in which 'you can help is by encouraging your relatives, friends and Christian leaders to read this book. Then they can contribute too!

Launch out into the deep

Jesus says,

> *'Come, follow me ... and I will make you fishers of men.'*
> (Matthew 4:19)

It is only in deep waters that the big fish are caught, and it is as you launch into the deeper waters of healing that you are most likely to see greater things happen yourself (cf. Luke 5:4). Launching entails making the most of opportunities for healing. We can see how Jesus was expert at launching. Whether He was faced with a comparatively simple need or one requiring a miracle, once it was time to minister He would step out in faith by opening His mouth to speak or reaching out His hand to touch. We have seen how His power and gifts can enable us to do the same. So when a young man once had the opportunity to minister, he did not hesitate, but launched out, declaring, 'If Jesus can do it, so can I!' (cf. Philippians 4:13).

When you launch out bear in mind our ultimate aim in doing this, which involves *thinking **big***. Our ultimate aim is not just the alleviation of physical, mental or emotional needs, speaking about Jesus, seeing people converted, ensuring they are filled with the Holy Spirit, nor their being faithful members of God's Church, nor seeing them witnessing and ministering effectively. Ultimately, the Christian's aim is nothing short of their total maturity in Christ (Ephesians 4:13). If you cultivate this big vision and pursue it, you'll be blessed in turn yourself and more able to help other people to do the same.

One step forward

At some of our gatherings I have invited people to take one step forward in their lives. It seems appropriate to invite you to do the same thing now in response to what you have read. One woman decided that her step would be to pray aloud for the first time. Another heard the Lord saying, *'Feed my lambs'* (John 21:15), and she offered to work with young people. However great or small your experience of healing, the next step is the one to take right now.

A lady called Kay did some late-night shopping one evening. On the way home she decided to pop in for fifteen to thirty minutes to the church where we were holding a service. Later on Kay told us:

'I'd only been there a few minutes when from the interpretation of a tongue I knew I'd be there for the evening! The Lord had already been speaking to me about my own need to stop playing about in shallow water and to go forward into the deeper waters. Then I heard him say at the service that He wanted to lead me gently into new depths. From then on the whole meeting spoke to me on this theme. I decided to take one step forward with Him, into the deeper water, and accordingly came forward for prayer.'

God will show you your next step to take if you ask Him. Step out in faith, and you'll find He'll give you all you need. You will not be disappointed, others will rejoice, and Jesus will be delighted!

Practical discussion questions

1. Share with your group about the next step that you are taking.
2. What is your vision of what God wants you to do in your group, church or beyond? Are you ready to do this? (1 Chronicles 4:9–10)
3. What are your hopes and prayers for the wider healing scene?
4. What have you most learned and gained from reading this book?

Epilogue

Healing the Jesus Way

The following summary applies to the Christian healing ministry but some of it is also appropriate for other forms of treatment.

Foundations of Christian healing

1. God's ability and willingness to heal
   (Matthew 14:14; Mark 1:41–42; Luke 4:18–19)
2. The Church's commission to heal
   (Mark 6:7–13; 16:14–20; Luke 10:1–12)

Areas of Christian healing

1. Relationship with God – salvation
   (Acts 2:21; 16:30–31; 2 Corinthians 5:20)
2. Physical healing
   (Matthew 10:1; Mark 16:17–18; James 5:14–16)
3. Inner healing – of mind, will and emotions
   (Psalm 147:3; Luke 4:18–19; Philippians 4:6–7)
4. Deliverance
   (Matthew 18:18; Luke 4:18–19; Ephesians 6:10–18)
5. Relationships
   (Genesis 45:1–15; Ephesians 4:32; Philippians 4:2–3)
6. Circumstances
   (Daniel 6:19–23; Acts 16:25–26; 27:22–26)

Methods of Christian healing (just some!)

1. The healing service
   (Acts 14:8–10; 1 Corinthians 14:26–32; James 5:13–20)

2. Holy Communion
   (Luke 22:14–20; John 6:51–57; 1 Corinthians 11:25–30)

3. Laying-on-of-hands
   (Mark 7:33–35; 16:17–18; Luke 4:40)

4. Soaking prayer
   (Mark 5:27–30; 8:22–26; John 9:6–7)

5. Anointing with oil
   (Mark 6:13; Luke 10:34; James 5:14)

6. Positive thinking
   (Matthew 21:18–22; Philippians 4:13; James 5:15)

7. Prayer counselling
   (Luke 4:18–19; John 21:15–17; Acts 8:26–40)

8. The spoken word
   (2 Kings 20:4–6; Matthew 8:13; James 5:15–18)

9. The message of knowledge
   (1 Kings 14:4–6; John 1:51; 4:18)

10. Confessing faults
    (Acts 19:18–20; James 5:15–16; 1 John 1:7–9)

11. Forgiving others
    (Luke 6:37; Ephesians 4:32; Colossians 3:13)

12. Deliverance
    (Matthew 18:18; Luke 4:18–19; Ephesians 6:10–18)

13. Encouragement to respond
    (John 2:5; Acts 3:7; 14:9–10)

14. Leading a balanced life
    (Proverbs 3:7–8; Mark 2:17; James 1:5)

Keys to Christian healing

If one or more of these major keys is lacking, this may be why a sick person has not yet been completely healed.

1. Faith
   (Mark 6:5; John 14:12; James 5:15)

2. Guidance
   (John 14:26; James 1:5; Revelation 3:22)

3. Love
   (John 13:34–35; 1 Corinthians 13; 2 Corinthians 5:14)

4. Gifts of the Holy Spirit
    (Matthew 10:8; Mark 16:17–20; 1 Corinthians 12:1–11, 28)

5. A release of power
    (Mark 5:30; Luke 5:17; Acts 3:12, 16)

6. A willingness to change
    (2 Kings 5:11–14; Mark 10:50–52; John 5:6)

Principles of Christian healing

The road to a balanced healing ministry

Breath has followed six principles, of which the initial letters spell 'PERSON'. Each sick individual is not just a case but also a person loved through and through by Jesus. The treatment is holistic and gentle but positive and powerful. Healing often results through combining treatment by ministry with medicine and/or therapy and self-help.

1. Point them to Jesus

He is the healer; it is His touch we have ministered; our faith is in Him and the results department is with Him. We have encouraged the person to keep his or her eyes on Jesus and give Him the glory (Hebrews 12:2).

2. Every case is different

God may heal the same person or condition in a different way from before. We have followed His guidance on each occasion, listening, asking questions, sharing gifts and using our experience (James 1:5).

3. Root cause (find it)

This is not always essential but often the person is not entirely healed until it is discovered. It is usual to pray about under-lying needs first; then physical healing is likely to follow (Mark 9:21).

4. Step out in faith

Once we have known it is the time to minister, we have offered Jesus' touch and, once we have begun to pray, the right words, the Lord's love, the healing power and other gifts required have begun to flow (Luke 5:4).

5. One step at a time

Unless we have known the full answer will come at once, we have prayed within our faith, a stage at a time. As our confidence grows, we can pray for bigger things till the goal is achieved (see Ezekiel 47:3–5).

6. No condemnation

Even if individuals have confessed a terrible sin we have not condemned them (cf. Romans 8:1). We do not condone the sin, but we have lovingly encouraged the person to repent and respond (cf. Acts 2:38, 43).

The results of a balanced ministry

1. Anything you ask

If we have followed these guidelines as the Holy Spirit has directed us, Jesus promises anything we ask in His name. We can expect Him to do the impossible, break the impregnable and heal the incurable.

2. Lasting effects

People have testified at our meetings to wonders Jesus has worked but also to some He did years ago, for, provided people maintain their healing with the safeguards I've described, the effects last.

3. Life in all its fullness

The initials of these results spell 'ALL', and St Paul writes, *'All things are yours'* (1 Corinthians 3:21). An abundant life is the ultimate desire of Jesus for all who trust Him to save, heal and satisfy (John 10:10). And it's our desire for you who read this too.

Practical discussion questions

1. Which areas of healing have you been most used in so far? Are there people in your church called to minister in other areas of healing?
2. Consider the same questions about methods of Christian healing.
3. Are any of the major keys in healing obviously lacking in your church? What is required to ensure a more effective ministry?
4. Are you satisfied with the results of your healing ministry?

Prayer

Healing Power

Lord we would prove Your healing power
  By trusting You this very hour
    To touch the sick ones here.
We know You are the same today
  And in Your mighty name we pray
    They'll feel Your presence near,
    They'll feel Your presence near.

Lord we would prove Your healing love
  By trusting You from heaven above
    To meet their every need.
We know You see deep down inside
  And that Your heart is open wide,
    So let Your Spirit lead,
    So let Your Spirit lead.

Lord we would prove Your healing power
  By trusting You this very hour
    To use our hands and tongue.
Your precious words these folk shall know
  And through our hands Your power shall flow
    While praise to You is sung,
  While praise to You is sung.

Lord we would prove Your healing love
  By trusting You from heaven above
    To drive all wrong away.
Let each one here be Spirit-filled
  And know he is Your Father's child
    And freedom find today,
    And freedom find today.

We praise You Lord for what You've done
  And for the work You have begun
    And all that is to come.
O grant that we may constantly
  The channels of Your healing be
    Until You call us home,
    Until You call us home.

Appendix 1

Terminology of Healing

The following terms are arranged in alphabetical order:

Charismatic healing This is healing resulting from supernatural God-given abilities. It is splendid if manifested with love and glory is given to God.

Christian healing This puts the emphasis on Christ as the healer, distinguishing the ministry from other kinds of treatment, whether helpful or harmful. It places healing in the context of the Church and the believer's everyday experience. It infers that complete healing will include a relationship with Jesus Christ, and demonstrates that Christians have something specific to offer. I believe this is the best title.

Counterfeit healing This amounts to any cure ultimately from the devil, whether or not the practitioners are aware of this. Satan has a counterfeit for every genuine gift of the Holy Spirit and he may deceive people with a false measure of healing. This especially issues currently through spiritism, the occult, other faiths and the broader New Age movement. Satan's healing is never complete, for genuine wholeness includes the healing of someone's relationship with God which can only result through repentance and faith in Christ (Revelation 3:17–20).

Divine healing This shows God to be the healer. But which god? Many false healing practices are linked with different divinities. 'Divine healing' is also a popular term with people who reckon doctors are unnecessary for believers and that all healing should issue from the Church.

Faith healing This is a popular term used by the media as a title for all kinds of healing involving laying-on-of-hands. But many 'healers' work independently of the church and expect people to trust in things other than the Lord. Some of these are associated with spiritism and the occult. 'Faith healing' may also infer that the sufferer must have faith to be healed. While

Christians encourage people to have faith in God (Mark 11:22), this is not always essential for physical restoration. The faith of others may be sufficient.

Genuine healing This is all true healing given by God, but we may need discernment about what is good and genuine. Doctors, therapists, even Christians make mistakes in diagnosis and treatment. But if the healing is beneficial to the person, is not contrary to the Scriptures, and is acceptable to Christian leaders, it's probably worth receiving. Whenever you want to know if anything is from the Lord, remember the simple advice: 'If you're not sure, *share!*' (2 Kings 20:8–11).

Health A state of complete well-being, involving a person's spirit, soul (mind, will and emotions), body, relationships and circumstances.

Medical healing This may use controversial surgery, it can be too drug-orientated, and the whole person may not be treated, yet it is often what God desires, and the healing that results can be regarded as coming from Him.

Miraculous healing This title is used rather sceptically by those scholars who think that all Jesus' miracles in the Gospels can be explained naturally and that either the healings there were psychosomatic or that the accounts were fabricated by the early Church. However, those who do believe in miracles need to be careful not to cheapen the word by using it for every little cure. The Bible distinguishes between gifts of healing and the gift of working miracles (1 Corinthians 12:8–10).

Natural healing The term can be applied to three types of physical restoration: (1) healing resulting after injury when the wound heals naturally; (2) healing resulting from release of energy within someone's body; (3) healing from using natural means/substances, e.g. exercise/herbs. Since God has made our bodies, we welcome natural healing but see it as insufficient for every need. Sometimes, too, the term 'natural healing' may be used for what is really a supernatural counterfeit.

Psychiatric healing Psychiatry can raise controversial questions: drugs just cover up problems, and the result may be less than real healing. But, when real healing results, this should be regarded as coming from God.

Spiritual healing This term is frequently used by all kinds of people for all kinds of healing through laying-on-of-hands. It is a term preferred by the British Confederation of Healing Organisations (which encompasses more than a dozen healing societies). While this contains a growing number of Christians, it includes a large number of people with spiritist leanings, a vast array of natural and psychic healers, and many who are New Age adherents.

Supernatural healing This sounds good, but when God works in supernatural ways He often uses natural means. The devil and his agents are responsible for counterfeit healing that is also supernatural, and may wear off.

Wholeness The meeting of every genuine need as far as is possible in this imperfect world. For Christians it includes the need to know Jesus.

Appendix 2

Therapies and Practices

The following therapies and associated practices are referred to in this book on the pages printed beside them. A practice which is not a therapy is often not part of a therapy either. If we regard it as questionable and it is a major factor in the practitioner's life or treatment we would normally advise a Christian client to consult a different complementary therapist.

Q denotes that a subject is covered throughout the answer to a question.

acupressure 83
acupuncture 74, 83, 98, 100, Q22, 151–152
Alexander Technique 83
anointing, oils 48, 57, 79, 81, 98, 111, 227
aromatherapy 79, 81, 91, 144, 154
astral projection 101, 163
astrology 99, 147, 154, 159, 166, 168
automatic writing 164

biochemic system 147
biofeedback 111
biophysics 98
birthstones 166
black magic 159, 161
  see also satanism
Buddhism 65, 99, 139, 213

channelling 180
chiropractic 79, 83, 100, 152, 218
Christian Science 163
clairvoyance 52
colour therapy 166
Confucianism 99, 139
contemplative meditation 62, 65, 67, 81, 101, 204

continuing professional development 153
counselling 21, 69, 79, 83, 85, 109, 112, 118, 124

dance therapy 81
dark areas 154, 215
diets 94
  see also nutritional therapy
dilution 148
  see also potentisation
divination 147, 154, 156, 160, 167, 170
dowsing 154, 160, 167
  see also pendulum swinging
dreams, dream therapy 80
  see also sleep

Eastern religions 66, Q22
energy medicine 74, 97–98, 100, 145
exercise 18, 27, 63, 81–82, 84, 94, 96, 134, 177, 233

family tree healing 86, 186, 189
fasting 80, 106, 187, Q31
food 79, 94
  see also nutritional therapy

fortune-telling 86, 99, 166

hatha yoga 86
health shows 215
herbs, herbal medicine 80, 83, 95,
    130, 134, 233
Hinduism 65, 99, 139
holistic health groups 99
homoeopathy 9, 11, 54–55, 74, 83,
    98, 140–141, 144, Q23, 152–153
horoscopes 166, 168
    see also astrology
humanism 66
humour 10, 12, 96, 203
hydrotherapy 96
hypnotherapy 53, 85, 134, 154

imagination 39, 64, 112
    see also visualisation
Institutions recognising therapies see
    Appendix 3
integrated health care 220
intuition 52, 114, 116, 135, 137, 163
iridology 111
Islam 103–104, 137–138

kinesiology 83, 91, 98

laughter 81, 121
    see also humour
law of cure 146, 149
laying-on-of-hands 10, 18, 37–38,
    48, Q8, 72, 75, 79, 85, 107–108,
    126, 130, 133, 198–199, 202, 204,
    213, 227, 232–233
    see also touch
leisure 96
    see also relaxation techniques
levitation 169
life coaching 17, 85
Luciferic Initiation 161

magic 24, 97, 130, 147
magnet therapy 84–85
manipulation 60–61, 82–83
mantras 65
Manual Lymphatic Drainage (MLD)
    84
massage 60–61, 81, 83–84, 92, 150
Materia Medica 146

meditation Q9, 81, 99, 101
mediums 86, 179–181
meridians 74, 83
mind over matter 53, 55, 86, 137
    see also suggestion
monism 99

National Register of Christian
    Therapists 18, 152, 210, 237, 239
natural healing 134–136
natural health centres 210
nature worship 165
    see also pantheism
nature, natural remedies 27, Q14, 99,
    134
naturopathy 84, 95–96
New Age movement 66, 89, 97, 99,
    139, Q35, 232
nutritional therapy 73, 79, 94–95

occult, occult healing 9, 12, 49, 68,
    98, 127, 130, 135, 139–140,
    142–143, 148–149, 153, Q25,
    162–164, 168–170, 188–189, 207,
    232
osteopathy 9–10, 17, 47, 60, 69, 79,
    82–83, 100, 140, 144, 152, 207,
    215, 218
ouija 143, 159, 163

PACT 12, 18, 100, 131, 133, 150,
    210, 241
paganism 99, 142, 165
palmistry 166
pantheism 99, 165
past-life regression 86
pendulum swinging 99, 167
physiotherapy 69, 82, 219
placebo Q7, 75, 77, 95, 145, 147
polarity therapy 85
    see also magnet therapy
positive thinking 52, 227
potentisation 147–149
prayer counselling 85, 112, 227
premonitions 116, 135, 163
prevention 60, 77, 94, 126
psychic experiences 101, 163–164
psychic fairs 215
psychic healing 86, 136–137, 159
psychometry 163

psychotherapy 79, 84, 134, 142
pyramid power groups 99

referral 133, 152, 218–219
reflexology 11, 61, 74, 79, 84, 98,
    100, 142, 153, 168–169
regulation 73, 95, 100, 218
reiki 135
reincarnation 86, 89
relaxation techniques 66, 80
research 54–55, Q11, 83, 98, 100,
    135, 218
rest 80
    see also relaxation techniques
rolfing 150

séances 86, 179
satanism 159–161
secularism 66
sensitives 180
shiatsu 83, 152
sleep 80–81, 96
sorcery 156, 160, 164
    see also witchcraft
soul travel 163
    see also astral projection
sound therapy 166
spiritism, spiritualism 86, 99, 159,
    Q29, 189, 232

spiritual healing 61, 80, 133–134,
    154, 233
succussion 148–149
suggestion Q7
superstition 165–166, 168

Taoism 139–140
tarot 86, 166
tea leaf reading 166
telepathy 52
touch 15, 35–36, 45, 55, Q8, 70, 75,
    79, 84, 91, 98, 100, 102, 127, 136,
    177, 184, 188, 199, 202, 221, 224,
    228
trances 85, 179, 189
transcendental meditation 62,
    66–67, 101, 159–160, 204

visualisation 40, 91, 112
vitamins 79, 95, 126
voodoo 168

witchcraft 99, 130, 156, 158–160,
    164

yoga 86

Zoroastrianism 166

Appendix 3

Institutions Recognising Therapists

This list includes institutions at which practitioners on the National Register of Christian Therapists have been trained.
This list is not exhaustive, but was supplied to Breath by the practitioners on the Register at the time this book was written.

Alliance of Registered Homoeopaths
Aromatherapy Organisations Council
Association of Christian Counsellors
Association of Light Touch Therapists
Association of Natural Medicine
Association of Reflexologists
Bayly School of Reflexology
Belfast Institute of Further and Higher Education
Bowen Therapy Academy of Australia
Bowen Therapy European Register
British Association of Beauty Therapists and Cosmetology
British Association of Chartered Psychologists
British Association of Nutritional Therapists
British College of Acupuncture
British Institute for Allergy and Environmental Therapy
British Medical Association
British Psychologists Society
British Register of Complementary Practitioners
Causeway Institute, Coleraine
Central Manchester College
Central School of Counselling and Therapy
Centre for Nutritional Studies
Chartered School of Physiotherapists
Chelsea School of Chiropody
Chimes School of Natural Therapies
College of Classical Homoeopathy

College of Nutritional Medicine
College of Practical Homoeopathy
Colonic International Association
Crawley College
Crusade for World Revival
Dartington College of Arts
Doctor Edward Bach Foundation
European College of Bowen Studies
Faculty of Homoeopathy
Fellowship of Homoeopaths
General Council and Register of Consultant Herbalists
General Osteopathic Council
Grace School, Nada
Guild of Complementary Practitioners
Hahnemann College (London)
Harlow College
Homoeopathic Medical Association (UK)
Institute for Optimum Nutrition
Institute of Allergy Therapists
Institute of Biodynamic Psychotherapy
Institute of Complementary Medicine
Institute of Counselling
Institute of Psychotherapy and Counselling (Westminster
    Pastoral Foundation)
International Correspondence Schools
International Federation of Aromatherapists
International Federation of Reflexologists
International Institute of Health and Holistic Therapies
International Institute of Reflexology
International Shiatsu Association
International Society of Professional Aromatherapists
International Therapy Examination Council
Kinesiology Federation
Life Coaching Academy
Lynden School of Reflexology
Martindale Trust
National Register of Christian Therapists
Northern College of Homoeopathic Medicine
North London Teacher Training School for the Alexander
    Technique
North West College of Homoeopathy
Oakdene College

Open University
Paula Martin School of Natural Therapies
Plaskett Nutritional Medical College
Reflexology Scholand and AOR
Register of Shiatsu Society
Revival School of Aromatherapy
Roller College
Royal College of General Practitioners
Royal College of Nursing
Royal College of Physicians
Royal Pharmaceutical Society
Salford University
School of Chiropody and Podiatric Medicine
School of Phytotherapy
Shirley Price Aromatherapy
Society of Homoeopaths
South East Kent Technical College
South Trafford College
Stewart Mitchell School of Complementary Health
Traditional College of Acupuncture
United Kingdom Central Council (of Nursing)
United Kingdom College of Life Coaching
University College Hospital
University of London
University of Ulster
University of Wales
Wessex College of Complementary Medicine
Westminster Pastoral Foundation

Appendix 4

Breath Ministries and PACT

Breath Ministries were founded by Reverend John and Mrs Christine Huggett in 1979 to encourage and promote healing and wholeness in the churches and beyond. Breath Fellowship Trust is their registered charity for healing, teaching and training.

PACT (Positive Approach to Complementary Therapies) was founded in 1995 as a branch of Breath to support Christian therapists and to provide teaching and guidance about complementary medicine.

John Huggett is available to speak to churches or groups of any size or form on any of the subjects in this book, in particular:

- **Getting healing ministry going**
- **Taking healing ministry further**
- **A positive approach to complementary therapies**

John also writes articles for periodicals and church magazines.

John's book *Six Keys to Healing* can be obtained by sending a cheque for £6.00 paid to Breath Ministries at the address below.

The National Register of Christian Therapists, published annually by Breath, can be obtained by sending a cheque for £3.00 to the same address.

Prayer Ministry from a Breath team member is available on request to leaders, or occasionally to other people when they are unable to receive such ministry in their own churches or localities.

Information about tours of the Holy Land can also be provided on request when these are possible and the circumstances are right.

Information about John's own hymns and songs can also be provided.

Breath Ministries
Weald House
10a High Street
Tunbridge Wells
Kent
TN1 1UX
England
e-mail: cjphuggett@btopenworld.com

What people have said about Breath

'It is a delight and privilege to commend the ministry of John and Chris Huggett, which, I believe, is done humbly and faithfully in the name of Jesus, and effectively for the glory of God and the extension of His kingdom.'

(*Bishop David Pytches*
formerly Vicar of St Andrew's Chorleywood)

'Anyone who has experienced John Huggett's conferences or ministry in recent years will know he is one of the best teachers on healing.'

(*Rev. Norman Howard*
former Warden, Lamplugh House Conference Centre)

'The Huggetts' ministry defuses myths and extremes, placing healing within the reach of both helper and sufferer, affirming the crucial central roles of Jesus Christ and the Holy Spirit.'

(*Doctor Heather Bassett*
Australia)

Bibliography

Benor, Daniel J., *Healing Research*, 4 vols., Helix

Church House Publishing, *A Time to Heal*

Coker, Robina, *Alternative Medicine – Helpful or Harmful?*, Monarch

Cowie, Ian, *Across the Spectrum*, The Handsel Press

Crook, Alan, *A Christian's Guide to Homoeopathy*, Winter Press

Dale, David, *The Love that Heals*, David Dale

Dearing, Trevor, *God and Healing of the Mind*, Bridge Publishing; *Total Healing*, Mohr Books

Drosnin, Michael, *The Bible Code* (Books 1 and 2), Weidenfeld and Nicolson

Fletcher, Eileen, *The Optimum Health Guide*, Spire Books

Harding, Ed., *What Christians Should Know About Sickness and Healing*, Sovereign World

Hurding, Roger, *Pathways to Wholeness*, Hodder & Stoughton

Huggett, John, *Healing in the Balance*, Kingsway; *Six Keys to Healing*, Kingsway; *Twelve Healing Hymns*, Breath Ministries

Huggett, John and Christine, *It Hurts to Heal*, Kingsway

Jordan, Hector W., *A Christian's Search for Health*, Vantage

Kefauver, Larry, *When God Doesn't Heal Now*, Thomas Nelson

Kraft, Charles H., *Deep Wounds, Deep Healing*, Sovereign World

Lawrence, Roy, *Finding Hope and Healing through the Bible*, Triangle; *The Practice of Christian Healing*, Triangle

Malkmus, George H., *Why Christians Get Sick*, Treasure House

McMillen, S.I., *None of These Diseases*, Lakeland

McNutt, Francis, *The Power to Heal*, Ave Maria Press

McTaggart, Lynne (ed.), *What Doctors Don't Tell You*, Thorsons

Mumford, Nigel, *Hand to Hand*, Hodder & Stoughton

Parsons, Stephen, *Searching for Healing*, Lion

Pearson, Mark, *Christian Healing*, Hodder & Stoughton

Pytches, David, *Come, Holy Spirit*, Hodder & Stoughton

Richardson, Cheryl, *Take Time for Your Life*, Bantam Books
Stanway, Andrew, *Alternative Medicine*, Penguin Books
Stokes, Terry, *Why Throw Out the Baby with the Bathwater?*, Terry Stokes
Temple, Rachel, *Medicine – the Christian Dilemma*, Rachel Temple
Times Supplement on Healing, An A–Z Guide to Complementary Medicine, 6 parts
Urquhart, Colin, *God's Plan for Your Healing*, Marshall Pickering
Watt, James (ed.), *The Church, Medicine and the New Age*, The Churches' Council for Health and Healing
White, Anne S., *Healing Adventure*, Logos International
Wimber, John, *Power Healing*, Hodder & Stoughton

Index

For therapies and associated practices see Appendix 2
Q denotes that a subject is covered throughout the answer to a question.

abilities 46, 123, 134–135, 137, 163, 186, 232
abuse 94, 113, 158, 161, 207
accountability 152
activity 23, 74, 159, 168, 211, 221
addictions 186
affected part 45, 58–59, 115
after-care 189
AIDS 69
allergies 94
alleviation of symptoms 72
  see also remissions
ancestral line 86, 186, 189
angels 27, 116, 119, 138, 170, 180
anger 21, 96, 146
animals 55, 58, 99, 145
anorexia nervosa 195
antibiotics 76–77, 110, 147
anxiety 21, 23, 146, 186
apathy 23
  see also ignorance
areas of Christian healing 78, 226
armour of God 172–173
arthritis 27, 108, 128, 175
assurance 42, 67, Q19, 153, 186, 200, 215
asthma 91, 95, 111
atmospheres Q32, 204
attitudes 21, 27, 32, 52, 95, 111, 186, 207
authority 31, 35, 48, 112, 119, 172, 183–188, 192–193, 198–199, 203

Bach, Edward 84, 141, 239
back pain 60, 82–83
Baker, Marilyn 81
balance 90–91, 93, 95–96, 99, 140, 219
baptism 46, 173, 197, 201
Barker, Joel 217
Beatles, The 62
Becker, Robert 74
Benor, Daniel 56, 75, 77
Beneviste, Dr 148
bereavement 112–113
  see also death
Bethesda, Pool of 32, 64, 177
Bible 20, 27, 37, 39, 52, 57, 64, 77, Q12, 93, 124, 145, 155, 157, 167, 169–170, 175, 177, 179–180, 186, 191, 197–198, 204, 223, 233
Bible Code 223
binding evil powers 185
blindness 19, 25, 32, 110
blood of Jesus 35, 85
body language 113
boldness 42, 48
bondages 29
  see also freedom
Brains Trust, The 183
brainwaves 75, 204
breakdowns 170
  see also depression
breast cancer 69
Breath Centre 92

Breath Ministries 12, 14, 17, 55, 78, 175, 208, 214, 217, 221, 228, 241
British Confederation of Healing Organisations 133, 233
British Medical Association 70, 76, 238
British Medical Journal 147
British School of Osteopathy 141, 212
Browning, Robert 217
Burrswood 69, 96

Callinan, Paul 148
cancers 30, 107
casting lots 167
catchers 204
chains 185
chance, luck 166–167
change 22, 29, 90, 178, 190, 204, 208, 228
channels 12, 34, 74–75, 83–84, 180, 195
chemotherapy 27, 145
children 14, 28, 30, 54, 57, 73, 104, 145–146, 170
cholera 74
Churchill, Winston 188
circumstances 21–22, 27, 30–31, 53, 78, 141, 144, 177, 192, 204, 221, 226, 233
cleansing, purification 35, 95, 187
clusters 131
coincidences 53
command prayers 48, 193
  see also authority
commissioning 57
communion 21, 57, 63, 90, 191, 221
compulsive behaviour 186
confession 190
confidence 52, 55, 64, 181, 194, 210, 218, 229
  see also boldness
confirmation 40, 45, 69, 117, 119, 126–127, 154, 202, 215
confusion 12, 139, 151
  see also misunderstandings
conscience 27, 211
control 24, 39, 66, 85, 88–89, 91, 98, 112

counterfeits 123, Q20, 167
Cowie, Ian 136–137, 159, 181
criticism 24, 91, 217
Crook, Alan 11, 54, 98, 100, 141, 145
cults 130, 163
cursing 170
  see also rebuking

deafness 19
Dearing, Trevor 6, 38, 61, 64, 164
death 17, 77, 105, 113, 116, 163, 180, 200
deliverance 10–11, 47, 78, 111, 127, 144, 164, 168–169, 172, 182, Q30, 195–196, 226–227
Department of Health 73
depression 21, 42, 81, 127, 158, 192
diagnosis 70, 72, 111, 132, 146, 154, 167, 233
digitoxin 145
diocesan councils of health and healing 17, 106
disabilities 30
discernment, discerning of spirits 11, 28, 102, 132, Q25, 169, Q28–30, 233
doctors 25, 27, 36, 43, 54–55, 60, Q10, 73–76, 90, 111, 132, 142, 147, 151, 164, 186, 207–208, 217–218, 232–233
doors opening and closing 27
Dossey, Larry 76
double blind trials 54
drugs 21, 32, 54–55, 70–71, 75, 84, 88, 92, 95, 98, 101, 147, 149, 184, 186, 204, 233
dualism 207

'earth-forces' 137
Eastern religions 66, 139
Eddy, Mary Baker 163
Edison, Thomas 143
Edwards, Nita 105
Einstein, Albert 148
electroacupuncture 74
encouragement 22, 90, 119, 149, 209, 213, 227
endomorphins 74

energy 54, 58–59, 61, 66, 75, 77,
    83–85, 91, 95, 97–102, 134,
    136–137, 148–149, 163, 181, 192,
    198–199, 207, 219, 233
enlightenment 66, 99
environment 18, 21, 60, 72, 93, 99,
    214–215
evangelism 45, 124, 213, 215, 221
evidence, proof, testing 30, 46, 54,
    62, 71, Q11, 99–100, 117, 135,
    149, 207, 218
evil 31, 48, 78, 89, 99, 135, 142–143,
    148–149, 156, 158–159, 161–162,
    165, 168, 170, 172–173, 182–185,
    187, 207
    see also Satan
evil spirits, demons 11, 31, 47, 115,
    161, 164–165, Q19, 181–183,
    186–190
exhaustion 84, 94
    see also tiredness
exorcism 11, 101, 159, 161, 169, 171,
    182, Q30
    see also deliverance
expectancy 24, 64, 217
experience 9–11, 20, 22, 26, 30, 33,
    41, 48, 51–53, 65, 90, 97, 106,
    111–112, 117–120, 130, 135, 143,
    153, 163, 172, 174, 178, 187,
    199–201, 207, 211, 219–220, 222,
    224, 228, 232

failure 175
    see also success
faith, unbelief 16, 19–24, 26–28, 30,
    33, 40, 48, 51, 55, 60, 71, 86,
    89–90, 107, 121, 124, 143, 147,
    165–166, 174, 202, 206, 211, 215,
    224–225, 227–229, 232
falling under the power 36, 44, 101,
    197, 199, 204–205, 209
false hopes 28, 39, 52
false prophets 118, 156
familiar spirits 170
fast foods 94
fear 14, 21, 23, 28, Q5, 90, 97–98,
    100–101, 139, 146, 161, 169, 173,
    184, 186–187, 206–207
feelings 44, 58, 61, 84–85, 91, 101,
    108, 116–118, 120, 125–126, 165,

    171–172, 177, 182–183, 189,
    197–200, Q33, 209
    see also physical sensations
fellowship 35, 95, 190, 210
first aid 81, 153
fitness 18, 61–62, 79–80, 84
    see also health
Fitzgerald, William 142
Fleming, Alexander 147
forgiveness 186
Forty Promises of Healing from
    Scripture 62
foundations of Christian healing
    226
freedom 39, 47, 112, 118
From Witchcraft to Christ 164
fruit 121, 144, 156, 166
Full Gospel Businessmen's Fellowship
    International 164
Full Gospel Church, Seoul 143
fullness of the Holy Spirit 20, 38,
    42–43, Q6, 131, 221, 224

General Osteopathic Council 152,
    239
genetics 69
genuineness 120, Q20
    see also counterfeits
ghosts 181
gifts 11, 15, 20, 23, 27–28, 33–34,
    37–38, 45–46, 48, 52–53, 80, 85,
    97, 101, 111, 114–116, Q19–21,
    158–159, 181, 198, 201, 221–224,
    228, 233
Grad, Bernard 56
greater things 6, Q1, 222, 224
    see also miracles
Green Pastures 210
growth 21, 23, 171
guidance 27, 80, 86, Q16–18, 150,
    156, 163, 165–167, 179, 194–196,
    227–228, 241
guilt 21, 111, 173, 186

habits 94, 186
    see also addictions
Hahnemann, Samuel 141, 145–146
Hammond, Sally 55
haunted houses 187
healing homes 80

Healing in the Balance   18
health   12, 17–18, 61–62, 70, 75,
      79–81, 84, 88–90, 92, 100, 102,
      214–215, 233
heat   56, 201
Heavenly Deception   163
Hippocrates   142
Hitler, Adolf   89, 188
Holy Communion   48, 227
      see also communion
Holy Land   29, 64, 223, 241
honesty   10
hospices   61
hospitals   74, 135
      see also doctors
humility   111
hurts   21, 113, 119, 210
hygiene   79
hypocrisy   35

iatrogenic disease   70
ignorance   206
immunisation   145
inadequacy   37
      see also success
Indonesian Revival   21
inhibitions   186
inner healing   21, 78, 112–113, 161,
      175, 182, 184, 226
interpretation   11, 28, 47, 116, 225
involvement   10, 17, 49, 88, 96, 162,
      169–170, 182, 188–189, Q35,
      219
Irvine, Doreen   164
It Hurts to Heal   17, 56, 126, 199, 213

jealousy   21, 32, 178
Jewish healers   138
Joad, C.H.   183
joy   31, 211
judgements   112, 139, 141, 143–144
Jung, Carl   152

karma   89
keys to healing   18, 26–29, 33, 103,
      227–228
knowledge   21, 28, 48, 54, 66, 79,
      Q18, 135, 162, 177, 181, 184,
      189, 197, 227
Kuhlman, Kathryn   197

Lancet, The   147
Lane, William   95
launching out   37–38, 224–225
leaders   17, 23, 34–35, 37, 43, 57, 90,
      107–109, 124, 126, 132, 150, 159,
      174, 217, 219–221, 223, 233
Legal and General   152
leisure   96
      see also relaxation techniques
lifestyle   18, 21, 60, 88, 94–95, 177
listening   63, 85, 107, 111–113, 157,
      169, 195, 228
Loehr, Franklin   55
London Homoeopathic Hospital   74,
      147
love   15, 27–28, 38–39, 42, 64, 78,
      118, 125, 131, 176, 179, 186,
      Q34, 214, 221, 227–228, 232

machines   58
Maharishi, The   62
medicine   9–10, 17, 25, 29, 33, 54,
      68–73, 76, 83, 85–86, 98, 100,
      102, 106, 139–140, 142, 145–147,
      153, 167–168, 220, 228
      see also doctors
memories   21, 28, 39, 42, 85,
      112–114, 186, 209–210
mental illness   11, 146, 169
methods of Christian healing   226
micro tens machine   36
miracles   Q1, 28, 30, 45, 214, 222,
      233
Missionary School of Medicine   149
mistakes   28, 37, 70, 132, 233
misunderstandings   71, 103, 125
mocking spirits   188
Moody, D. L.   49
Moonies   130, 163
Mormons   130
mysteries   30

name of Jesus, name of God   9–10,
      48, 71, 138, 169, 172, 177,
      184–186, 188–189, 203–204
National Association for Primary
      Care   220
National Federation of Spiritual
      Healers   133
National Health Service   73, 219

nations, healing of 223
near-death experiences 163
Newlands Park Natural Health
   Centre 210
Newton, Isaac 142
no condemnation 208, 229
nursing 124

obedience 16, 32, 120, 206
old age 25, 104
Olympic Games 82
Omand, Donald 187
one step at a time 26, 229
oppression 158, 171
ordaining 57
   see also commissioning
origins Q22, 208, 219
overworking 26
   see also activity

pain 32, 36, 47, 54, 57–58, 60, 74,
   90, 104, 108, 113–115, 117, 163,
   177, 180, 192
palliative care 30, 61
peace 57, 112, 146, 163, 184, 186,
   222
penitence 57
   see also repentance
perfection 30
persecution 43, 141
   see also criticism
persistence, perseverance 22, 196
pesticides 94
physical sensations 36, 44, 58, 61,
   91, 101, 108, 116–118, 120,
   125–126, 165, 171–172, 182–183,
   189, 197–200, Q33, 209
picturing 40, 59, 112
pioneers, blazing trails 6, 14–18, 217
place memories 181
plants 55, 80, 92, 148
pollution 93
posture 83
power 10, 12, 17, 28, 34, 37, 39, 44,
   46, 48, 51–52, 58, 97, 101, 108,
   119, 125, 133, 136, 158–159, 162,
   165, 169, 172, 176, 182, 189, 193,
   Q32, 200–204, 207, 209, 211,
   215, 221, 224, 228
power evangelism 214

praise 16, 46, 55, 64, 107, 173, 183,
   189, 193, 198
prayer 10, 18–19, 22, 33, 36, 46, 49,
   51, 55, 57, 59–61, 63, 65, 71–72,
   75–76, 79–80, 90, 98, 100,
   103–105, 107, 113–114, 116, 119,
   130, 143, 162, 174–176, 187–188,
   Q31, 197–201, 219, 221–222,
   225
prayer ministry 60
preaching 18, 34, 212
premature deaths 105
principles 25, 140, 150, 157, 228
progress 18, 26, 30, 66, 95, 164, 174,
   221
   see also change
promises 20, 64, 105, 109, 229
prophecy 23, 28, 42, 116, 120, 166,
   198, 209
protection 85, 134, 170, 180, 188,
   190, 207, 215
provision 106, 220
psychiatry 21, 184, 233
Pullinger, Jackie 47
Pytches, David 178

quality, quality of life 18, 22, 70, 95,
   126

radioactivity 74
re-creation 24, 126
reassurance 42, 205
   see also assurance
rebuking 170, 172, 176
reconciliation 35
relationships 30, 35, 42, 78, 85, 222,
   226, 233
release 49, 176, 185, 189
   see also freedom
relevance 214
remissions 30
repentance 32, 215, 232
reputations 40
resentment 21, 27, 32, 112, 177, 186,
   190
respect 40, 119, 157–158
   see also reputations
response 54, 95, 98, 136, 150, 199,
   224
responsibility 89–92

resting in the Spirit 36, 44, 101, 197, 199, 204–205, 209

results 18, 21–22, 28, 33, 51–52, 55, 58, 70, 73, 75, 77, 98, 130, 145, 148–149, 156, 186, 193, 198–199, 228–229, 233

resurrection 89

retreats, retreat centres 80

revelations 27, 109, 114–120, 171

revival 15, 19, 223

Richards, John 131

root causes 60, 82, 88, Q17
  see also origins

Satan 15, 25, 31, 37, 49, 66, 99, 128–129, 147, 158, 161, 163, 165, 168, 170–171, 176–177, 187–189, 192–193, 203, 207, 232

schizophrenia 115

scientology 130

scriptural meditation 62–63, 65

Scripture 27, 78, 82, 86, 89, 99, 117, 155–156
  see also Bible

self-confidence Q7

self-help 228

self-improvement 99

selfishness 32–33

Shakarian, Demos 164

sharing 37, 53, 57–58, 90, 118, 124, 131, 157–158, 174, 214, 228

side-effects 70, 146, 177

Siegel, Bernie 73

signs and wonders 16, Q1, 222
  see also miracles

silence 44, 47, 53, 65, 109, 116, 136, 198

sin(s) 29, 32, 35, 63, 93, 97, 104, 135, 141, 160–162, 167–168, 170, 177, 186–187, 190, 204, 206, 208, 229

Six Keys to Healing 18, 128, 193, 241

slain in the Spirit 204

Smith, Cyril 148

smoking 85, 186

soaking prayer 59, 108, 114, 120, 227

speaking 37, 44–45, 64, 106, 117–121, 198, 212, 224–225
  see also spoken word

spells 156

'spirit-forces' 137

spirit guides 102, 179–180

spirits 63, 65, 86, 114, 117, 129, 158–159, 164, 169, 171, 180–181, 188–189

spirits of infirmity 31, 170, 176

spirituality 95, 212

spoken word 61, 79, 186, 227

standards 100, 152, 158, 211

Steiner, Rudolf 147

Stemp, Malcolm 140, 159

Still, Andrew 140

still, small voice 124

stress 21, 75, 81, 92, 110

success 54–55, 126, 135, 145, 213

suffering 25, 30–31, 39, 80, 93, 126, 128, 176, 194

supernatural 10, Q1, 27, 46, 51, 63–64, 76, 91, 101, 116, 124, 134–136, 156, 159, 165, 167, 189, 232–234

Taylor, Hudson 149

teaching 10–11, 14, 17–18, 20, 26, 28, 42, 46, 78, 82, 133, 139–141, 143, 161–163, 219, 241

teams 35

tears 26, 105, 114, 119

telepathy 52

Temple, Rachel 74, 140

tension 21
  see also stress

Teresa, Mother 89

terminology *see* Appendix 1

thanksgiving 193

therapies and practices *see* Appendix 2

three days 105, 175

thumps 201

time, timing 9–10, 22–23, 26–27, 30, 36–37, 63, 70, 76, Q16, 116–117, 119, 127, 157–158, 171–172, 174–175, 177, 193–194, 196, 223–224, 228–229

tiredness 94

tongues, speaking in 11, 28, 44, 46–47, 49, 59, 101, 114, 116, 125, 197, 200–201

tools 26, 111, 155, Q31–33

training 14, 17–18, 36, 60, 72, 100, 111, 128, 140, 147, 149, 152–153, 212, 241
two in agreement 192

ultrasound 55
unclean spirits 170
unhealed Q2, 104, 175–176

Vineyard Fellowship 178
vision, visions 12, 23, 27, 116, 120, 204, Q36
vital force 97–98

waiting, waiting on the Lord 109, 116
walking in the Spirit 27, 44
warnings 10, 219
We Are All Healers 55
Wesley, Charles 173

Westminster Pastoral Foundation 142, 239–240
wholeness 25, 30, 67–68, 86, 103, 106, 116, 128, 215–217, 219, 223, 232, 234, 241
Wigglesworth, Smith 153
Wimber, John 172
windscreen wiper verse 35
wisdom 28, 41, 45, 111, 116, 120, 142, 158
worse after treatment or ministry 36, 175–176, 182
worship 63, 65, 81, 108–109, 137, 143, 173, 189, 197, 204, 215, 222
see also praise

X-rays 69

Yellow Pages 151

If you have enjoyed this book and would like to help us to send a copy of it and many other titles to needy pastors in the **Third World**, please write for further information or send your gift to:

**Sovereign World Trust
PO Box 777, Tonbridge
Kent TN11 0ZS
United Kingdom**

or to the **'Sovereign World'** distributor in your country.

Visit our website at **www.sovereign-world.org** for a full range of Sovereign World books.